Dr Anna Sandiford is an independent forensic science consultant. She provides advice on forensic science for a wide range of clients, including barristers and solicitors, insurance companies, private investigators, private clients, police forces and intelligence agencies. As an expert witness, she has an overriding duty to assist the Court impartially on relevant matters within her areas of expertise.

Dr Sandiford has worked in forensic science since 1998 and has been involved with cases throughout New Zealand, the UK and, on occasion, the Channel Islands and the Cayman Islands. She is director of The Forensic Group, a forensic science consultancy based in Auckland.

EXPERT WITNESS

DR ANNA SANDIFORD

HarperCollins*Publishers*

HarperCollins*Publishers*

First published in 2010
by HarperCollins*Publishers* (New Zealand) Limited
PO Box 1, Shortland Street, Auckland 1140

HarperCollins*Publishers*
31 View Road, Glenfield, Auckland 0627, New Zealand
25 Ryde Road, Pymble, Sydney, NSW 2073, Australia
A 53, Sector 57, Noida, UP, India
77–85 Fulham Palace Road, London W6 8JB, United Kingdom
2 Bloor Street East, 20th floor, Toronto, Ontario M4W 1A8, Canada
10 East 53rd Street, New York, NY 10022, USA

National Library of New Zealand Cataloguing-in-Publication Data

Sandiford, Anna, 1970-
Expert witness / Anna Sandiford.
ISBN 978-1-86950-875-3
Includes bibliographical references.
1. Forensic sciences—New Zealand. 2. Forensic scientists.
3. Criminal investigation.
I. Title.
363.250993—dc 22

ISBN: 978 1 86950 875 3

Cover design by Xou Creative
Cover images by thinkstockphotos.com
Typesetting by Springfield West

Printed by Griffin Press, Australia

70gsm Classic used by HarperCollins*Publishers* is a natural, recyclable product
made from wood grown in sustainable forests. The manufacturing processes
conform to the environmental regulations in the country of origin, Finland.

Contents

About the author

This book is about my job and the casework in which I have been involved. I didn't plan on this being my job, but that's the way it's turned out. Being a forensic scientist is a very serious matter and is taken very seriously in day-to-day life. What forensic scientists do has a direct impact on people, which will affect those people and those around them for the rest of their lives. This is the aspect of the job with which most people are familiar because of media portrayal, television dramas and such like.

However, as in any job, there is a certain degree of monotony that comes with spending hours being stuck in traffic jams and dealing with bureaucracy. At the other end of the spectrum are the amusing things that come out of investigating death, destruction and general law-breaking (it is a well-known phenomenon that people who face the most traumatic situations every day manage such difficult circumstances by trying to make light of them and finding things funny; it's human nature and a safety mechanism). The humdrum and the amusement are the aspects people don't consider about forensic scientists' jobs, but they're the things that help us remain sane and functional.

I'm hoping this book will provide an indication of how forensic science is applied in a practical sense and give you an idea of what the job actually entails. With the exception of the David Bain case (which is pretty much public property these days), I have blurred the facts slightly or changed details (or just been thwarted in providing exact detail due to some of these things happening so long ago) so that the people and cases I write about can remain anonymous. While some people may think they recognise cases or situations, rest assured, every attempt has been made to prevent this happening.

My purpose in providing case examples is to demonstrate how the forensic science was applied or what happened in a situation, not to point fingers at particular criminals, lawyers or other individuals. The case examples are purely illustrative. I also refer to forensic scientists as expert witnesses or just experts. In this book, these terms are interchangeable.

When I'm not writing books or blog posts, I work as an independent forensic scientist and researcher. As far as qualifications go, I hold a Bachelor of Science (Honours) degree in Geology and a Master of Science in Micropalaeontology (microfossils), both from the University of Southampton, England. I also hold the degree of Doctor of Philosophy in Geology and Palynology (pollen analysis) and a Postgraduate Certificate of Proficiency in Forensic Science, both from the University of Auckland. Some people would say that eight years as a student is far too many, but it just took me a while to find out what I wanted to do with my life.

I am Director of The Forensic Group, a company which aims to be New Zealand's most comprehensive independent forensic science consultancy. I am accredited with The Academy of Experts, a United Kingdom-based international accreditation organisation, and I am a Professional Member of both the Royal Society of New Zealand and the United Kingdom Forensic Science Society. I am also Secretary of the New Zealand Independent Forensic Practitioners' Institute. All these memberships mean I am governed by several codes of conduct and ethics and that I am required to be impartial in my work.

I have been involved with forensic science since 1998, and until 2002 I was a forensic science consultant in New Zealand. Between 2002 and June 2008 I was employed first as a forensic science consultant, then subsequently a senior forensic science consultant and ultimately practice manager with a forensic science consulting company in England. As part of those roles I prepared more than one thousand reports on a variety of evidence types, largely for the defence but also for the prosecution. I also peer-reviewed and assessed a further one thousand-plus reports in a wide variety of forensic scientific fields.

A significant part of my role over the past 10-plus years has been the review of other scientists' files as a peer-reviewer for accreditation purposes and as an expert appointed by either the Crown or the defence. I have reviewed dozens of files from ESR in New Zealand, all of the laboratories of the Forensic Science Service and LGC Forensics, the two main service providers in England and Wales, as well as casefiles from independent laboratories in England and Wales plus police forensic science laboratories in Scotland, the Channel Islands and the Cayman Islands.

One of my roles as a senior forensic science consultant is coordination and management of cases involving more than one evidence type. I review the scientific evidence, liaise with experts, manage the disclosure documents, organise the logistics of examination and re-examination of items and samples, arrange testing, organise Legal Aid funding and manage the general progress of the work until completion.

I have given evidence in court on more occasions that I can remember, but not as many times as I have actually been asked to attend court, but there's more about that in later pages. I regularly provide scientific advice to police forces, particularly in the United Kingdom.

In my capacity as a research scientist, I have published papers in national and international independently peer-reviewed scientific journals and I was a reviewer for the international scientific publication, *Journal of Forensic Sciences*. I am actively involved in forensic science research in conjunction with the School of Environment, University of Auckland, where I hold the position of Honorary Research Associate. I have lectured at the University of Auckland and at Anglia Ruskin University, Cambridge, England, in science and forensic science. I have also given science and forensic science presentations at various national and international scientific and non-scientific conferences and also at the England and Wales police Drink Drive conference. I spend quite a lot of time speaking to non-scientific groups including professionals, schools and general interest groups. You may have noticed that I keep referring to England and Wales instead of just writing 'the United Kingdom'. The reason is because the laws that govern England and Wales are different from those in Scotland; the Scottish don't use non-Scottish experts unless absolutely necessary, such as in cases involving drug traces on banknotes because there's no one else who can do that sort of work. Ireland (Northern and Republic) also works in different ways with different police forces and different approaches. While it may seem cumbersome to write England and Wales, it is more accurate and, as a scientist, accuracy rocks!

As an expert witness I understand that my overriding obligation is to the court and not to those instructing me. This means I won't say something in court that isn't true to the best of my knowledge and belief.

Acknowledgements

It's been a long road and I thank my mum and my gran for their contributions along the way. I know what I'll be like when I'm 89, because I look and sound like my mum, who looks and sounds like her mum. Patch, Baa and John have also been good influences, even if they're not aware of it.

I also thank all the people (there are a lot of them and they know who they are) who have taught me on this journey, including all the geological-, scientific-, anecdotal- and life-experiences. I thank Nick Powell for pointing me onto this career path in the first place and also John and Kathy Manlove who have kept me here despite enormous challenges. Mark Horrocks and I keep each other on the forensic pollen path and he's taught me a lot, including how to identify New Zealand pollen grain. It's debatable if I've taught him as much, but I like to think so.

I also thank Jason for letting me be who I am and for everything that we have gained together.

Finally, Lorain Day and HarperCollins for giving me this opportunity to write. I've enjoyed it; it's a cathartic experience and I thoroughly recommend it.

Prologue

I am standing in a large, old, unfurnished room with a partially carpeted concrete floor and only one exit. A convicted murderer stands between me and the exit. There's nowhere to hide. I'm kneeling on the floor with my head bowed down, close to the unmoving dirt and dust around the edges of the room. The air is hot, humid, heavy, oppressive. Sweat slowly rolls down through my hair and I hope he can't see it — it's a sign of weakness and I don't want him to know about it. I can feel him looking right at me. I feel self-conscious and I don't know whether I should meet his eye. As I look around, I see blood on the floor. Fresh blood. I'm so close to it I can taste it at the back of my mouth. I know it's fresh because I saw it spill onto the floor. I try not to breathe it in but I can't help it, it's everywhere I look. There are bloodied sock prints across the entire floor, made by the convicted murderer as he paced about.

This isn't just any murderer, he's notorious, infamous. He was tried and convicted of five murders and sentenced to a mandatory life term in prison, minimum parole period of 16 years. Yet here he is after 12 years, standing between me and my only way out. This was my own choice. I invited him into this room and now I'm in here with him. I know the door's unlocked but there's a chair pushed up against it to stop it being opened from outside. The man brought someone with him, another man, who is forthright and solidly built, determined.

The questions in my mind could be, am I afraid? How can I get out of here alive? The actual question is, how big are his feet? The man in question is David Bain. The man with him is Joe Karam. I am here because they have asked me to assist the defence team for his retrial. I am here because I am a forensic scientist.

Now that we know why I'm in this situation, let's look at that scene again. I am standing in a large, old, unfurnished room with a partially carpeted concrete floor and only one exit. The carpet has been put down by me and consists of strips of different types: a section of wool-rich cut pile here, a section of synthetic cut pile there. There are also long sheets of paper underneath the edges of the carpet to prevent blood getting on the concrete. Unsealed concrete is absorbent and it'll soak up the blood, which I don't want.

David Bain does indeed stand between me and the exit. That's because he's been told to stand there while I finish getting everything sorted out. I'm kneeling on the floor with my head bowed down, close to the unmoving dirt and dust around the edges of the room. I'm doing this so I can label each carpet section so they don't get mixed up.

The air is hot, humid, heavy and oppressive. I'd forgotten just how hot it can get in Auckland in summer, particularly so in an enclosed space with a metal roof, baking like an oven. Sweat slowly rolls down through my hair and I really hope neither he nor anyone else can see it — if it drips on my working notes it will make the paper damp and difficult to write on. No windows are open and there's no ventilation — there's a Burmese cat outside desperate to get in because she can smell the blood, and she's yowling as only a cat of Far Eastern persuasion can yowl. If she gets in then we'll never get her out and she could cause havoc with the tests.

I can feel David Bain looking at me. Not surprising really, seeing as it's me who's directing him when to put his foot in cow's blood. I don't know whether I should meet his eye. I don't normally have anything whatsoever to do with defendants. In civil cases the word *defendant* can be replaced with *respondent*. Whatever they're called, I usually don't have any contact with them. Having to meet a defendant is unusual and I have to keep it impersonal. Unfortunately, this means I have to border on being rude, which goes against my instincts — I hate it when people are rude to me; there's just no need for it.

As I look around, I see blood on the floor. Fresh blood, which I can taste at the back of my mouth because I'm so close to it. I know it's fresh because I saw it spill onto the floor. Well, to be honest, it didn't exactly spill, more of a pour-into-a-tray than a spill. It's fresh because I collected it from a supplier this morning, who got it from an abattoir even earlier in the day. It's whole blood so that it mimics as closely as possible the way whole human blood behaves when it's liberated from the body. 'Whole blood' is the term used to describe blood from which nothing has been removed. Serum, platelets, fibrinogen and other components of blood can be removed from it to be used for a whole range of things, mostly in the biomedical field. In fact, the company that provided me with this blood usually provides antibodies, serum and other biological mixes for diagnostic testing purposes. They clearly thought I was mad when I asked if I could have some whole blood so we could walk it around the floor using feet and socks.

There are bloodied sock prints across the entire floor, made by David Bain as he paced about. This is a good thing. We're testing the length of the sock prints he would make if he walked in blood and then walked across carpet.

The door's unlocked but there's a chair pushed up against the door to stop it being opened from outside. This is to stop anyone walking in by mistake and also to prevent accidental admission of said cat.

The man who accompanied David Bain is Joe Karam, who I think is fairly described as forthright and solidly built; he looks as if he might have played serious sport at some point in his life. He was, in fact, an All Black and he looks determined because he is. He's also very focused. He's fought long and hard for this retrial and it's approaching at a rapid pace. When David Bain and Joe Karam arrived to do these sock-print tests, it was two weeks before the scheduled start of the trial. Luckily for me, the start date was delayed by another two weeks, until 6 March, which gave me a bit more report preparation time. Never rush a scientific report, especially if it's to be used in court, more especially if it's going to be used in what has been termed the 'trial of the century' by the media. It strikes me that it's the trial of the century because the media has made it that way, but what do I know? I wasn't here when the killings occurred in 1994, I wasn't here for the first trial or the appeal. I'm not even a real Kiwi.

This man isn't just any murderer, he's notorious. This is true — at this stage he was one of the most, if not *the* most, notorious murderers in New Zealand history. When he was

22, he had been convicted of murdering five members of his family.

According to the Crown case, after he had shot four of his family, David Bain went out and completed his paper round before coming home, waiting in an alcove in the sitting room for his father to come into the house from the caravan where he was living, before shooting his father, turning on the family computer, typing his father's fake suicide message and then calling the police.

In 1995 David Bain was tried, convicted and sentenced. In 2007, the Privy Council in London determined a gross miscarriage of justice had occurred. The New Zealand Solicitor General ordered a retrial, which took place in 2009, between 6 March and 5 June.

So here they both are. David Bain has obligingly put his foot in cow's blood, walked around some pieces of carpet and gone home. Joe Karam has departed as well. I'm left with the prospect of shifting sections of carpet to a photographic laboratory so they can be sprayed with a blood-enhancing chemical and photographed under special lighting conditions. Because this is mid-summer, it doesn't even think about getting dark until 10 p.m., which means it's going to be a late night. Luminol, the blood-enhancing chemical I am testing with, needs to be used in darkness. The photo studio doesn't have full window coverings so we have to wait until it gets dark. By the time the sock prints have been sprayed, measured, sprayed again and photographed, it's 2 a.m. and I'm tired, dehydrated (standard laboratory practice: no drinks or food) and, not for the first time and not for the last, I'll wonder what the hell possessed me to think that being a forensic scientist was such a bloody good idea.

❖

Because the general perception is that I work exclusively with dead people, I'm asked now and then if I've ever been aware of my own mortality? In a word, yes.

I've always been pretty good at disassociating my conscious brain from my work. That's largely helped by not having to deal with actual suspects or victims very often. From that point of view, my role is quite unique. Where else in the criminal justice system do people involved with crime routinely have absolutely nothing to do with the people involved in those crimes? Think about it: everyone else in the criminal justice system has direct contact with people who were involved with the actual events. They might be victims or suspects, convicted criminals or the wrongly convicted or the families of all of those people. Fire fighters, police officers, social workers, judges, court officials, barristers, solicitors, crime scene examiners, pathologists, prosecution forensic scientists, the list goes on. Even in insurance work, the private investigators, insurance company representatives, legal counsel for the insurance companies — the one thing they all have in common is that they generally have direct involvement with the people involved in the key events. Independent experts who are instructed some time after the initial events are probably the only people who don't.

If you happened to be an expert working largely for criminal defence lawyers, and if you played your cards right, you could spend practically your entire career avoiding direct contact with the nasty end of crime. Of the thousands of drink-drive related statements I have written as an expert for criminal defence or insurance lawyers, I can count on the fingers of one hand the number of defendants/claimants with whom I have actually had any kind of conversation. And that was in those rare cases when they insisted on having their breath alcohol elimination rates estimated. Such circumstances involve them coming into the office at 9 a.m. and drinking the best part of a pint of vodka, so we can measure their breath alcohol level at regular intervals. There was also a nerve-wracking situation at court once, when I was stuck in a windowless interview room with a defendant, his dad and their solicitor between me and the door, but generally speaking it's been trouble-free.

So I guess it's been easier for me to block out the horror of what is involved in real life crime, and it certainly makes it much easier to interpret the facts in a dispassionate and impartial way. Imagine my shock when I realised I should consider myself lucky to be alive.

I didn't have one of those near-death experiences I hear about. One such story was recounted to me by a woman I know, who was living in a remote location. She and her husband encountered a distressed man who said his wife had threatened him with a knife. The poor distressed man was sent off with the kindly woman on her own, so that he'd be safe from the knife-wielding wife, while the husband went to see if he needed to call the police. The kindly woman took the distressed man to her house and settled him in the kitchen for a nice cuppa. Turns out that rather than being the victim, the man had been the attacker. He'd had a pop at his wife with the knife. The kindly woman now found herself on her own with a madman in a kitchen — with knives. She had to try to remain calm and handle the situation before he lunged at her with a Sabatier. She survived to tell the tale, which is more than the man's attacked wife — he murdered her two weeks later, stabbing her to death.

I did, however, find out that I had spent six weeks camping, in a tent on my own, in an area where, and at a time when, a serial killer was at work. Most disturbing of all was that, at the time, the police didn't even know they had a serial killer on their hands.

In 1990 I was at the end of the second year of my under-graduate degree in geology. As part of the course we were required to undertake a six-week field-mapping course. Officially, this involved going to a selected location and applying recently learned geological skills to an actual area of countryside, of which we had no prior geological knowledge. We were to collect data, then use this to interpret the under-lying geology to produce a geological map of the area. In reality, for me this was a prime opportunity to wander around the countryside, do some fieldwork and have a blast enjoying Belgian beer and cakes. I chose to go to the Ardennes region of Belgium with four fellow geologists. The other options were Southern Ireland (structurally complicated — not my cup of tea), Spain (we'd been on a field trip to Spain the year before and I fancied a change) or somewhere in South America (too many poisonous spiders). Looking back on it, I guess I was never going to be a field geologist. Of our party of five, I was one of three who camped, and the only one who camped alone. Two shared a tent, although they denied it, and the other two shared a caravan.

I was reading Stephen King's *It* at the time, which features a particularly nasty clown. As anyone who has read the book will know, it also involves some spooky stuff with hands reaching out of stormwater drains and dragging people off to a nasty demise. Unfortunately, to get from the camping area at the bottom of a valley (total number of tents at any one time: two) you had to cross a bridge over a wide stream. Very picturesque in the daytime. Scary as you like at night. I never, ever crossed that bridge after dark. I was clearly deluded that the flimsy, flapping, woven, waxed and non-cutproof tent sides would protect me from marauding monsters, mad clowns and raging murderers.

Three of our crew were very dedicated and set off early in the morning to get in a full day's mapping. My friend Julia and I, on the other hand, had decided we'd do it the easy and, more importantly for self-justification, safe way. Neither of us was keen on being in the field on our own but we weren't really taken that seriously when we raised our concerns before we left England. To combine safety with speed (always rely on a woman to multi-task and do things the quickest and most effective way) we borrowed her boyfriend's car. He was one of the keenies who was out at the crack of dawn trudging up hills with his freckly English legs flashing through the grass. We drove around both our allocated field areas and when we saw a rock outcrop, we hopped out of the car, quickly dashed across a field or two, took some measurements, hopped back into the car, on to the next site or café, whichever came first. We covered a huge amount of ground and got lots of data in a fraction of the time. Perhaps doing the fieldwork by car saved our lives.

At the time we were on this field trip, a husband and wife were driving around the Ardennes luring girls and young women into their van to be raped, murdered and dumped. Some of the bodies were found in the grounds of a castle the husband, Michel Fourniret, owned. He was to become known as the Ogre of the Ardennes, and in 2008 was found guilty of murdering seven young women between 1987 and 2001, in and around the Ardennes region of the French-Belgian border. He is also suspected of having murdered others, including in 1990 a young British woman, Joanna Parrish.

I was blissfully unaware of all of this until I was researching this book. Had Julia and I not teamed up and taken the car, either one of us may have become a victim and I could have become involved with forensic science for all the wrong reasons.

Chapter 1

Forensic science: the real world

The ultimate lesson is that science isn't special — at least not any more. Maybe back when Einstein talked to Niels Bohr, and there were only a few dozen important workers in every field. But there are now three million researchers in America. It's no longer a calling, it's a career. Science is as corruptible a human activity as any other. Its practitioners aren't saints, they're human beings, and they do what human beings do — lie, cheat, steal from one another, sue, hide data, fake data, overstate their own importance and denigrate opposing views unfairly. That's human nature. It isn't going to change.

Michael Crichton, 2006

Viewing life as a forensic scientist is very different from any other perspective. In a previous life, I was a geologist. My view then was far more pleasant. I didn't see landscapes as simply a collection of trees, hills, streams, cliffs and beaches, but with a mental overlay of geological maps, each part of the country a different colour depending on the age and type of rock beneath the surface. I saw it as geological processes in action, the changing face of the earth, volcanic history beneath my feet. Weather wasn't just a set of clouds, it was circumpolar winds, jet streams, Hadley cells. It was lovely and airy and if I had to choose a colour to describe it, I'd choose green.

As a forensic scientist I now look at things from another perspective. Every open window is a potential entry point for a criminal, every set of handwriting is about the sweeps and curls peculiar to that writer, every crumpled car panel is a message about the cause, every alcoholic drink has a residence time in the body. The world I inhabit now is often brown and grey, but that could just be lack of sunlight (there's a lot of paperwork and not many windows in the laboratory).

I've stopped writing anything vaguely important on pads of paper because of the impressions left on underlying pages. If I need to write down any secrets I make sure I have the single sheet of paper on a hard surface like formica or concrete, not wood or paper. I drive with my car doors locked (bag snatchers at traffic lights), I park my car in well-lit places, preferably with CCTV cameras, which I try to turn and face without drawing too much attention to myself. If I can avoid it, I never open the front door at the usual point of contact, lest I smear any important fingerprints. I don't put any personal information into rubbish bins and Facebook details are a no-no.

It sounds extreme but it's just the way I've learnt to be.

The world of forensic science is a very serious one and forensic scientists are a guarded lot. As an expert witness at court you can't let anything out in case the 'other side' gets a whiff of your personality and somehow capitalises on that in order to win their case. In the United Kingdom, New Zealand and certain other countries we are, after all is said and done, working in an adversarial system. And regardless of what anyone says, this system is heavily influenced by legal personalities and game-playing.

Because of the prevailing perception within this system that showing personality is a weakness, I believe forensic scientists are the only witnesses at court who aren't allowed to be real people.

If you asked a jury who were the most memorable people they saw in a case, I bet they'd say the ones with personalities — because they remember them and are therefore more likely to remember what they said. I don't *actually* know what they'd say because I've never spoken to anyone who's been on a jury for any of the cases with which I've been involved — it would be unethical. Now I come to think about it, I don't think I even know anyone who's been on a jury.

The inability to show personality is a conundrum, especially for an expert witness like me. I'm told I'm good at my job (I'm a modest sort) and I get enthusiastic about it and I like to talk about it in a non-specific manner (no names are mentioned). Court is not the place to talk about your knowledge, except in a very controlled manner. Number one rule for counsel: never ask a question to which you don't know the answer. This is supposed to apply when examining or cross-examining but it also seems to extend into the time before the hearing or trial. I've lost count of the number of times I tried to tell defence counsel before a trial that my evidence wasn't going to be helpful to their client and then when I said something unhelpful in my oral evidence they got all lemon-sucky-faced about it and refused to talk to me afterwards. You can't tell some people, as my mother would say.

The upshot of this is that I love my job and I love giving presentations, talks, seminars, workshops, training courses — you name it. I also accept that giving evidence in court or in front of a tribunal is a critical part of the job and, although I won't go as far as to say I enjoy it, it's something I hope I do well. I am experienced in the ways of the court and I know when not to speak beyond what I've said and I understand the limits of what I need to say. It's a skill all good expert witnesses nurture and hone and all good barristers and solicitors recognise when they see it in the witness box.

For example, there's no need to waffle on about how tandem mass spectrometry works unless it's directly relevant to the issue at hand. Otherwise it's boring for everyone in the court and, as a witness, you lose your audience's attention. If you've waffled on about your beloved tandem mass spectrometry and everyone's half asleep and counting down the seconds until break time, no one will be sufficiently focused to notice when you say something interesting or of relevance, such as: *Ninety-five per cent or more of English banknotes have traces of cocaine on them.*

It is also incredibly difficult not to speak to fill a silence; it's a well-used interview tactic. It's a challenge to finish what you want to say and then stop, especially if you're being cross-examined and counsel wants you just to fill the silence with something that might be of assistance to their case. Just say what you have to say. Stop talking. Silence. Wait. Someone will do something but it doesn't have to be you.

Here is an extract from a court transcript which demonstrates when not to get too overinflated and relaxed when giving evidence as an expert witness. The expert is being cross-examined by the QC for the other side (a QC is a

Queen's Counsel, a level of title awarded to only some senior barristers):

> *QC:* You wouldn't take the silencer off before you shot yourself, would you?
> *Expert:* I probably wouldn't shoot myself.

Laughter within court including, alarmingly, from the expert witness himself. At this point I knew it was going to go badly for the expert but oh so well for the barrister.

> *QC:* I would hope you wouldn't but the tragedy is ... that a lot of people who are seriously depressed do ... commit suicide, that's the tragedy, isn't it?
> *Expert:* That's correct.
> *QC:* It's not a laughing matter, is it?
> *Expert:* No, it is not.

I was right. Expert: nil, QC: 1. The expert lost credibility as a result of that short exchange, because everyone in the court went through approximately the same mental thought processs:

Ha ha, that's funny. Oh, no it's not. That barrister bloke's got a point. It's not *really* funny. Feel a bit embarrassed. Hope no one's looking at me. I'll look at that bloke in the witness box instead. Blimey, glad I'm not him; he looks gutted. I'll try looking serious to show I wouldn't laugh at something like someone shooting themselves. Fancy an expert saying that and laughing. Not very professional. What did he say just then? I missed that last bit ...

An expert should keep their personality in check in the witness box, no matter what the question. Sometimes, though, it's very hard to resist the temptation to say something smart. You have to remember that particularly in serious cases such as murder, the court proceedings are being transcribed into what is called the trial transcript (or a similar name, depending on the country). It's therefore not good enough to point to something and say, *the sample came from there*. The transcript must reflect what actually happened so that anyone can come back to it, possibly years later, follow what was happening and what was being discussed at any given point without having had to be present. Instead of saying, *the sample came from there*, it has to be described in terms such as, *in photograph 123, the sample was taken from the area shown in the top right hand corner, which was approximately five centimetres from the left hand edge of the blanket.*

I gave evidence in a case once where I was holding a photograph of a piece of carpet. The barrister said to me: 'Could you just describe what we see in the photograph marked, *Piece of carpet*. What is that a photograph of?'

It sounds like a ridiculous question because the court has just been told I took a photograph of a piece of carpet, they've been shown the piece of carpet (I'm holding it), here's the photograph of the piece of carpet that has been referred to as *Piece of carpet* and now I'm being asked to say what the photo's about.

So I said, 'A piece of carpet.' I knew I shouldn't just leave it at that because it sounded cheeky, so I left it a beat and carried on, but even though I wasn't looking at the jury, I could see a few grins out of the corner of my eye.

It's not just me, though. There are other examples, including this one, where an expert was giving evidence in relation to a drug case.

> *Lawyer:* What makes you say that the heroin was not a product of England?
> *Witness:* Climate would make it difficult.

I even heard a lawyer ask a witness, 'So, how old is your 16-year-old daughter?' The witness's face was a picture — she clearly thought the lawyer had lost the plot. This was, of course, a result of the lawyer following one of the basic rules of questioning witnesses during a trial: never ask a question to which you do not know the answer. He knew the answer but unfortunately it just so happened to come out of his mouth in the form of a ridiculous question.

Trials are very well organised events. Particularly at the level of serious criminal charges, they are meticulously planned by both sides, prosecution and defence (civil cases are often even more complicated). The lawyer is often asking one thing but their mind has already skipped ahead five minutes in time so their mouth can be on automatic and they don't always hear the bloopers. An example:

> *Lawyer:* What is the nature of the injury to your client's left shoulder?
> *Witness:* The injury is to his left elbow.

Had the lawyer asking the question been listening to the answer, he would have realised his mistake. Unfortunately, his brain had skipped forward and he hadn't heard the answer and didn't register the amused response to his question or the bemused response when he didn't notice what was happening.

Sometimes, people don't realise that what's in their witness statement is total cobblers. In drink-driving cases people are so desperate to keep hold of their driving licences they'll say anything. If they even looked at what they were saying, they might realise what they're asking the court to believe.

In most of the drink-drive cases with which I was involved in England I would have to point out, very politely, that some things might not seem very believable and that the magistrates might take a dim view. If a defendant pleads guilty early on, before the case gets to trial, they can often receive a reduction of as much as a third off their sentence. Some people would, however, insist on going the whole hog and, in my humble opinion, were never going to have a snowball's chance of being found not guilty. Here is an extract from a defendant's witness statement. He was charged with drink driving but his defence was that he had to drive because it was an emergency: *I was in an emergency situation. I needed to get her home, and as my friend commenced her fit, I consumed a third pint of lager.* If it was that much of an emergency, call an ambulance! I'm sure his friend would much rather know that if she has another fit, those around her will dive for their mobile phones, not think, *Shit, I've got a full pint — that's a bloody waste. I'll neck it before I help her.*

Of course there are legal definitions about what is or is not 'evidence'; there are laws of evidence and law students are specifically taught about evidence law. I don't propose to discuss the technicalities — there are plenty of legal text books to do that for me. Evidence to non-lawyers, though, is a different thing entirely and confusion often occurs when people get mixed up about what is classed as evidence in court. Someone with whom I used to work in England once recounted a story to me about one of his first experiences in court. He'd used the word 'evidence' in his report when talking about what he'd deduced after examining whatever it was in the laboratory. The judge leaned towards him and said, 'Young man, it is not for you to tell the court what is evidence. Evidence is what I allow to be heard by the jury in my courtroom. Until I allow it to be heard and accepted in my courtroom, what you have in your report are scientific findings and nothing more.' That told him.

There are all kinds of legal arguments that can be tossed about before someone is allowed to get into the witness box and give evidence, be they an expert witness or a bystander who saw a car drive off from a shooting. Even then, what a witness has to say needs to be judged to have reached certain standards before the witness can get into the witness box. Each jurisdiction has its own standards that the witness testimony must reach before it can be heard and *accepted* in open court. New Zealand's recent implementation of hearsay rules has been interesting — even though a witness may have very good information to tell the court about what they heard someone say, if it doesn't accord with the hearsay rules, it's not allowed to be presented as part of the case.

The moral of the story is: don't presume that what you've written will be accepted as evidence. It's only evidence if it's accepted as such by the judge or, as often referred to in legalistic terms, the trier of fact. A scientist's findings are exactly that — their findings. Oh, and never upset the judge — not a wise move, whichever way you look at it.

Chapter 2

Remind me again, how did I get here?

A t the time of writing, I am 40 years old and five feet eight inches tall, with longish blonde hair. It's going grey, but you can't tell unless you get too close, in which case you'll be in my personal space and I'll have to move away. Unless I'm showing you my grey hair to demonstrate how having kids and being a full-time forensic scientist caused me to go grey overnight. I've always wanted to be six foot tall, but it never happened. My brother is six foot four but it's wasted on him; he moans about being too big to find a motorbike that fits him properly. He also moans about the diminutive size of aeroplane seats, but he's not alone on that one.

Although some women wear heels to add extra height, I stopped doing that after I gave evidence in Oxford Magistrates' Court. The court set-up was very strange, or at least that's how I remember it. In England, Wales and Scotland, we stand up to give evidence unlike New Zealand, where the usual protocol is sitting down. Only once did I give evidence sitting down in England, and that was when I had to do some blood alcohol calculations in the witness box when I was seven months' pregnant. I couldn't physically reach the pen and paper I'd placed on the shelf inside the witness box where they keep the

Bible and oath cards. The judge asked if I'd like to sit down and I was relieved to say yes. It's like going to the house of one of your granny's friends — you don't sit down in an English judge's court unless invited to do so.

This particular witness box had a very low front. It seemed to come up to mid thigh, and it's high off the ground so you look down on counsel and the central court area. On this day however, I was wearing long black boots with four inch heels, so the edge of the box was about knee height. All I could think about was not wanting to lean forward too much in case I toppled out over the front and landed on the prosecution counsel; I had a touch of the vertigo thing going on. It was a typical English court situation — everyone ignored the elephant in the room, which in this case was the obvious discomfort of the expert witness (me) with the situation in the witness box. My evidence wasn't of any significant consequence as I was basically confirming what the prosecution was saying — that the defendant's account of alcohol consumption was so off the wall that had she consumed as much as she was saying, she would probably have been dead.

To add insult to injury, I'd been late arriving in Oxford, had struggled to find a parking space and ended up putting the car in some faceless, grey, underground municipal dungeon. In my rush, I'd parked so far away from the court I had to catch a taxi to get there from the car park. Oxford has one of those hideous we-hate-cars attitudes and actively discourages vehicles in the city centre. All well and good if you're a local or on a coach trip from Birmingham but a pain in the proverbial if you're in a rush and trying to park. The problem was that when I'd finished teetering over the front of the witness box at court,

I had no idea where I'd left the car. It was pouring with that special sort of grey, cold rain that soaks through your suede boots in 30 seconds flat. I was very late home and very grouchy.

But back to how I ended up in Oxford with inappropriate footwear and a hidden Skoda.

I think it was all just the roll of the dice. I started off training as a geologist and had an absolute blast in my undergraduate years, charging around the European countryside looking for fossils and measuring dips and strikes (rock-related measurements). There had always been an assumption that I would go to university, and I never even thought to challenge it. I just went off to Southampton when I was 18 and came back when I was 21 and overdrawn. Well, my mum will tell you I came back more often than that, usually with a couple of bags of laundry, but I did (mostly) do the washing myself.

As any graduate will tell you, a simple Honours degree is not enough to get you anywhere, so I needed to be more conscientious, do more studying and gain more qualifications. With this at the forefront of my mind, I returned home to the family nest, where I lived rent-free while stashing away whatever cash I earned as a legal secretary. After six months of hard saving, I had a quick look through the university prospectus and promptly went off travelling around the world.

Although I had a great time overseas, when I came back I still needed qualifications and a career plan. So I went back to Southampton to do a Master of Science degree, paid for by my long-suffering mother, because my first degree was average and I wasn't eligible for funding assistance.

Towards the end of my first degree and throughout

my Masters I specialised in sedimentary rocks, micro-palaeontology (microfossils) and palynology. Palynology is, very basically, the study of microscopic material formed of extremely chemically resistant material, usually pollen grains of seed plants, spores of ferns and various other microscopic particles (we usually refer to them collectively as 'pollen'). In the oil industry, chemical processes are used to extract pollen from rock samples and cores of material brought up from underground using long drills.

Fossilised pollen can help oil engineers 'see' their way around underground. By examining sequences of rocks and noting the way in which the microfossils vary in different rock layers (in conjunction with many other sophisticated techniques), it is possible to build up a three-dimensional picture of the sediments and structures beneath the ground surface. Once an engineer/geologist identifies the rock layer through which they want to drill or construct, it's a matter of examining the microfossils in that layer as drilling progresses to make sure the drilling stays in the direction it's supposed to. The tunnel that runs under the English Channel between England and France was kept on track partly by using micro-fossil analysis of the rocks being dug out. Back then, studying micropalaeontology was a traditional way into the oil industry or engineering geology.

I had another great year doing my Masters but by the end of the course, the oil industry had bottomed out and many top-level geologists and palynologists had been made redundant. There was no way the oil companies would give a job to a fresh post-graduate like me. Plus I would have had to do helicopter training, and that was a no-no. Did I fancy being plunged into a freezing cold swimming pool of water while strapped into the frame of a helicopter, just to see if I could get out alive? Strangely, no, I didn't. I know plenty of people who have done it, but they're real geologists.

Instead I spent some time living in the Canary Islands holiday resort of Tenerife, in that most classy of areas, Playa de las Americas. Anyone who has ever been to Tenerife or in fact anywhere like Ibiza, Majorca, Costa del Sol or Costa Brava will know these places are infested, and there's no cure. They are hopelessly infested with that most terrible of diseases — *Brits Abroad*. With knotted hankies on their heads (it's true), white and red suntans, drinking enough lager and alcopops to float a ship round the world, the British on holiday are a curious breed. I feel qualified to say that because not only did I work with them, I was one of them. Only once mind you, in 1994 for a week in February. It was such good fun I decided I'd like to live and work in Tenerife, which was a mistake of course, because life as a worker in a holiday resort is far removed from life as a tourist.

It wasn't the shift work or long, late hours that put me off living in Tenerife; it was the alcohol and drugs people poured into themselves. I couldn't stand the endless swilling and related drunkenness and the clatter of pill-popping all around me; some people should have had a childproof cap instead of a head, given the number of pills they popped every day. One day I just decided I'd had enough, I couldn't stand seeing it any more. There are only so many times I can put up with stag parties throwing up in the street or drunken women shrieking at each other and staggering about on high heels or watch helplessly as a pickpocket relieved yet another drunk of their wallet. You couldn't even go for a swim unless you left someone up by the towels on the beach because sometimes even a wet, sandy towel was pinched.

Having worked with holidaymakers at their worst and then working in England in a soul-destroying job looking after cashpoint machine engineers (it was the job that was soul-destroying, not the engineers), in 1996 I moved to New Zealand. I rang the University of Auckland not long after I arrived. The conversation went something like this:

> *Me:* 'I have a Masters degree in pollen analysis. Do you have any PhD projects going that I could do?'
> *Them:* 'Yes. It has a grant as well. When do you want to start?'

Unbelievable but true nonetheless. Doing that PhD was the best and worst experience of my life. Never has anything been so draining, with me working 16 hours a day for the last two years because I had to get a job and work full time as well as try to finish it. As anyone will tell you, a half-finished PhD is worse than not having started one at all, so you have to finish it, no matter how difficult it might become because of other circumstances. So I finished it and promptly had two consecutive bouts of flu, which lasted two months.

Unfortunately, towards the end of my PhD I decided a life in academia was not going to be for me, certainly not at that stage. Some would say that perhaps it would have been useful to know this before I started but them's the breaks, I guess. I really enjoy research but achieving a permanent, full-time job as a lecturer is not just about research ability or preparing lectures. It's about fighting for funding for your projects. Without funding you have no research projects; without research projects you can't attract postgraduate students and you haven't got anything to publish. These days, it's all about how many papers you can publish and how many other researchers cite your papers in their research papers. The advent of the Internet and electronic publishing of research papers means that the number of times your papers are cited in other people's publications can be tracked electronically. You are then automatically compared with your colleagues, not only in your own department or educational institute but also globally. Talk about pressure.

During the final years of my PhD I became interested in the application of pollen to solving crime. I attended a one-day course on forensic palynology where I met a man who was to become a colleague, who was also a geology graduate but had retrained in forensic science. He suggested I take the forensic science course at the University of Auckland. It was a total eye-opener. Before then I'd never done anything that felt so right for me, but forensic science was just exactly that. Geology was good and I enjoyed it, but I never saw myself working as a geologist. Forensic science on the other hand, well, it was just so logical and simple. The analytical techniques and the equipment used in forensic science are broadly the same as those used in geology. The basic science was easy to understand because I'd covered all of it during my years at university. Here, finally, I had found what I wanted to be when I grew up. At the age of 30, I decided I wanted to be a forensic scientist.

The next step was to get an actual job, which is tough in an industry where jobs are about as common as hen's teeth. I worked as a consultant in Auckland for a while, which meant I did casework experience without my employer having to commit to employing me full time, then decided I needed to go back to England.

It wasn't that I decided England was the best place for me but I had been living in New Zealand for six years by that time. I love living in someone else's country but it was crunch time. A lot had changed in my life since I'd moved to New Zealand in 1996 and I didn't know whether I was in New Zealand for the right reasons. I needed to leave because I was trapped in a depressing cycle where, even on a sunny day, it felt dark.

So I hopped online, searched New Scientist Jobs and there, calling my name, was a job as a forensic science consultant in Cambridgeshire, England. I emailed them my CV and the partner rang to ask me to come for an interview. It was kind of casually said, as if I could catch the 12.42 train from London and be there in time for afternoon tea. As it was, I packed a carry-on bag and checked in at Auckland International Airport for a week's round-trip to England. I doubt if these days I'd be allowed on a plane to London with just hand luggage, but other than checking that I hadn't accidentally left a 30-kilo suitcase in the car, the lady on the check-in desk gave me my ticket and off I went.

I'd also set up an interview with West Mercia police as a crime scene examiner, so I went to both interviews in the one week. I was 45 minutes late for the first interview because I became stuck behind a tractor, whose driver had absolutely no intention of letting pesky cars get past him on country roads. He was happily sitting on his bouncy tractor seat, grubby hat plonked on his head, piece of straw bobbing up and down in his mouth. I know it sounds clichéd, but clichés have their basis in truth and here was Farmer Giles, real as a cow pat. The reason I know he was chewing straw was because he kept turning round to look at how many cars he had behind him. Maybe it was National Tractor Car-Trapping Day. It was uncanny that when he turned around, it was always on that one bit of road when there would have been enough gap and forward view to pass him, if only the tractor hadn't drifted over the central line of the road. Anyway, the interview went well and I managed to make it home *sans* tractor interference.

I was also late for the second interview in Cambridgeshire. It doesn't look that far on the map from Bristol to Cambridge, but it's hideous. Too many years overseas had made me forget the horror of the M25 London orbital motorway. A car crashed in front of me, pin-wheeled to the roadside, and not one person stopped. Not because we didn't want to, but because it's impossible to extricate one's vehicle from the relentless, sluggish flow. When it's busy, traffic on the M25 has a special magnetic quality — you just can't break free and there's no hope of returning to the flow once you're out of it. Thankfully, in my rear view mirror I saw a police patrol car pull up just as I was crawling out of sight of the shocked driver. I rolled on towards the A1 and eventually got to the interview a mere two hours late. I loathe being late so I was cross with myself, embarrassed and stressed. It's not a good look and as I waited in reception with the office girls checking me out and casting eyebrow-wiggling glances at one another,

I was pretty sure I'd blown it before I'd even started talking.

Luckily for me, I was offered both jobs and, even luckier, I took the job in Cambridgeshire. I say that not because the CSE job would have been bad, because in a lot of ways it would have been an excellent career move. I say it because after I arrived in England a mere four weeks later to take up said new job, I found out I was seven weeks pregnant. With pregnancy came a super-sensitive sense of smell and I just know I would have vomited on a crime scene if I'd taken the CSE job. As it was, it was a close call on other occasions, particularly a long-distance cannabis cultivation case in South Wales.

Part of the job of the independent forensic scientist in England and Wales involves frequent travelling from the office to scientific laboratories around the country to examine items previously examined by the prosecution's experts. The way the system works is similar to that in New Zealand. An enquiry comes in from a lawyer asking for a review of some scientific aspect of a case, usually the prosecution expert's findings. We provide an estimate of costs, which has to be agreed by the Legal Aid people before we can start work. Once we're advised that Legal Aid has been approved, we go off to the lab, look at the items, go home, write a report, send a bill and, sometimes, go to court to give evidence. Sometimes, it felt as if our job was just rubber-stamping what had already been done, at other times there was more to it. In this particular cannabis cultivation case the police had raided a property and seized a whole load of cannabis plants.

In a case where a cannabis growing operation has been raided by the police, not all of the plants will be sent to the laboratory for examination. As scientists, we rely on the police accurately recording what was at the scene either by photographs, drawings and/or written notes. In some cases, scientists from a laboratory will go to a scene, but it depends on the particular case.

With this case only the police had attended the property. They seized dozens of plants from a hydroponic growing operation (a hydroponic operation is where the plants aren't grown in soil but are fed by nutrient-rich water pumped around their roots). Of those plants, they sent 12 to the laboratory for examination, each one sealed in its own brown paper sack. Once at the lab, the plants were taken out and dried, and most labs have a special drying room for this very purpose.

As I am sure many pregnant women will tell you, some smells are worse than others. For me, the assault on my nasal passages caused by walking into the lab's drying room was just too much. The sweet, heavy smell hit me like a smack in the face. I nearly passed out on the spot. The problem was that, at this stage, I didn't know I was pregnant. I just thought I was feeling rough, maybe coming down with a bug.

In the early days of my forensic science career, I went along to science laboratories as an assistant to my boss. Basically, he got to do all the good stuff and play with the exhibits while I had to write notes and keep up with his rapid narration. On this drugs case, it was just the same: he played with the plants and I wrote the notes. We were in that room with those plants for more than two hours. We had to examine them to check they were cannabis, photograph them, check the other scientist's case file, reweigh the leaf material, reweigh the flowering head material, repackage everything, chat with everyone my boss knew at the lab and stop for a cup of tea in the staff canteen. By this stage I couldn't bear the smell or taste of tea — iced water for me, thanks.

After all this in a small, stuffy, windowless, airless room, trying to impress my boss of only three weeks, I was feeling decidedly pale. My skin was damp, my eyes were dry, my hair was clinging to my scalp, my conversation was at the level of grunting, my writing was illegible. Even my hands were rebelling; cannabis plants are hairy critters and when they're dry, they shed sharp little spines all over the place. As I was writing, the hairs, which were being scattered liberally by my boss's shredding of the packaging, were showered all over the writing area and the paper. The hairs were grinding into my skin as I wrote and were unbearably itchy. By the time I'd finished writing I was smeared with a fine dust of powdered cannabis.

As was often the case, we had driven to the laboratory separately. After an interminable amount of time, he finally zipped off in his BMW and I headed off slowly in my Ford Focus, slumped in the driver's seat like a bag of old spuds. I got about 10 kilometres down the road, still feeling vile, but also surprisingly hungry. I stopped at a supermarket, ate some food and then promptly fell asleep in my car in the car park for two hours. How to explain a late arrival back at the office? It's amazing the number of roadworks that spring up all over the motorway system, particularly if two different people are travelling back to the same place along two different routes ...

As you can see, I took a somewhat circuitous and less-than-conventional approach to my chosen career, but it can be done both more cheaply and more quickly. I do, however, always recommend reading around a subject before committing to it, particularly something like forensic science, which has a tendency to be surprisingly gruesome when you're least expecting it, so here are a few suggestions: *Henry Lee's Crime Scene Handbook*; *Stiff: the curious lives of human cadavers* by Mary Roach and *Death's Acre: inside the legendary 'Body Farm'* by Bill Bass and Jon Jefferson (see reference section for full details).

Because so many people are influenced by programmes like *CSI* there is, as I've said before, a perception about forensic science — it's sexy, intriguing, indescribably useful and vital for case solving. So when people say they can understand why I do it because of their impression from TV programmes, it used to throw me into a bit of a spin although now I realise it's a great way to get people interested in science and also a good way to start a conversation at a party early in the evening when no one knows what to say. To me, forensic science is science at its most basic. It's been stripped down to the absolute bare bones because that's what happens when you give evidence and that's how you should write a report — so that it's totally justifiable, easily explainable and can be understood by anyone. There's no question of developing a new technique and bounding into court to give evidence in the next appropriate case — the method has to be tried, tested, approved by one's scientific peers, published in the relevant scientific publications and so on. In fact, this is exactly what the recent US investigation into forensic science in the United States has found — that not enough of the forensic science being presented in court has been through the same peer-review hoops as science in the academic arena. I wouldn't even think of trying to offer expertise and advice in a case with a method that wasn't tried and tested: I'd be torn to shreds by a good cross-examination and I'd probably never be instructed by the lawyer again. It would take a certain kind of barrister to allow such a gay-abandon approach to a case and at the end of the day, lawyers have their client's best interests in mind; they don't want to run any unnecessary risks. This is particularly so in criminal defence cases where many lawyers try to minimise the number of witnesses they call because, after all, it's the prosecution's job to prove beyond reasonable doubt, not the defence's job to prove innocence. Although sometimes I wonder if observers understand, or want to understand, that distinction.

Research science is a totally different game. It's about pushing forward the boundaries of science, getting into scientific and politico-scientific battles with colleagues and co-workers, competitive funding runs, and finding corporate dollars to fund risky research projects. Forensic science to me is the total opposite of all that. It shouldn't be about taking risks and pushing the boundaries of science because we are talking about a legal system that requires a standard of proof beyond reasonable doubt or, at the very least, on the balance of probabilities. If it's not reliable or repeatable, there will be problems even being allowed through the courtroom doors to give evidence, never mind the next step of having it accepted into evidence.

Keeping up with changes in forensic science and matters that are relevant is a mammoth task, particularly now that I'm running my own consultancy. I remember back in the days when scientific advancement in the media was pretty much limited to one or two major items a year, or so my remnant teenage brain reminds me. We used to have a programme called *Tomorrow's World*. I think it was on Thursday evenings, probably after *Top of the Pops*, and it showcased the latest in popular science developments. One night, the presenters were clearly beside themselves with excitement about the new development they were showcasing. Usually, they had feeble-minded attempts at science revolutions, some of which seemed embarrassing to demonstrate (I shan't name names because that wouldn't be nice.) Tonight, though, they had a box on the table. It was a box with a glass-fronted door. The magic thing about this box was that it heated things with nothing more than the power of water molecule vibration. What they had on the table was — drum roll — a microwave oven! Look at that, audience! You can put some water in the microwave, press the button and voila! Hot water! And that was the science advancement for the *year.* These days, science is changing on a day-by-day, minute-by-minute basis.

I have a blog, which is syndicated to New Zealand's largest science blog network (Sciblogs.co.nz). Because I'm a member of Sciblogs, I feel compelled to explore things of relevance and report them. This means I spend a sizeable portion of my day trudging the web (surfing just isn't the right word — it doesn't involve skimming across the surface and it doesn't involve being by the beach), checking Google Alerts, checking Twitter, Facebook, news sites, science sites, online publications — the list is seemingly and probably literally endless, because it just starts all over again tomorrow. Some people love it — that much is evident from the number of blog posts they put up every week and the online following they have developed, but sometimes it's so *exhausting*. Please bear this in mind if you read my blog — some tough trudging went into that last blog post ...

In summary, it's been a long and winding road to get to where I am and the road ahead is no less wiggly. I just hope the next 20 years will be as interesting.

Chapter 3

The nitty-gritty of the job

The expert witness performs two primary functions: 1) the scientific function — collecting, testing, and evaluating evidence and forming an opinion as to that evidence; and 2) the forensic function — communicating that opinion and its basis to the judge and jury.

Sapir, 2007: 'Qualifying the expert witness: A Practical Voir Dire', *Forensic Magazine*, February/March

Forensic science is a bit like love: it's a many and varied thing, sometimes it's the best thing since sliced bread, other times you wonder why you ever bother. Although that's where the similarities end.

As I said at the very start of this book, I want to give you an indication of how forensic science is applied in a practical sense and an idea of what the job involves. In order to do that, I should explain what the job actually entails. As with a lot of jobs, the only people who really understand what I do are other people doing the same thing. Even people (non-forensic scientists) with whom I have worked closely for extended periods of time still only have a snapshot image of what I can actually do.

The reason for that is because I am instructed (legal term for being briefed) in cases for a specific purpose relating to that particular case; no single case provides the opportunity to showcase everything my colleagues and I can do.

When I say I'm an independent forensic science consultant it's a bit of a mouthful but it's accurate, and that's important when your day-to-day job involves working with people who interpret words for a living. In a nutshell, my job is to make sense of science.

What I don't do is what they do on the TV. I don't even do the same job as forensic scientists who work for the prosecution or the police, and I certainly don't see dead bodies all the time.

However, what I've discovered while trying to describe my job is that it's nigh on impossible to generalise about what I do — if I break it down into interesting examples, I'd have to write an enormous book just to try to describe it all *and* cover everything my job involves. The problem with descriptions of what I do is that the specifics of casework are very different depending on whether it's criminal, insurance cases, civil litigation, family court cases or one-off projects, or if it's for training or giving lectures, seminars, workshops and presentations, even though the basic scientific approach is the same. One of the roles scientists like me have is generally being the ultimate quality control check. If the scientific report and its background can withstand independent scrutiny then the work has been done well by the other side's scientists. It's usually the case that the work is fine, but there are times when the work isn't up to muster — and it's up to me to check it and report what I find. Simple as that. Other times, I consider alternative hypotheses presented by my instructing party. I might also be the only expert involved in a case (such as drink-driving cases), but we'll come to all that later.

In general terms, the job involves reading documents, preparing reports, occasionally attending laboratories, occasionally undertaking original work, and giving evidence in court. Reading that last bit back, it sounds incredibly boring, which is exactly what a geology colleague of mine said recently when I gave a presentation to the local Auckland GeoClub. The thing is that, compared with pure scientific research, the application of science in a forensic context must seem unbelievably boring because it appears very simple. In reality, of course, it is anything but. If we look at what other scientists do then maybe you can see where it gets interesting. Scientists working in traditional 'prosecution expert roles' are those who are usually undertaking original work and testing. One of the most interesting examples would be somewhere like the Defence Science and Technology Laboratory (DSTL) in England. In this sense, 'defence' refers not to the criminal justice system meaning of the word but rather the 'Defending of the Country' meaning of the word, and definitely with capital letters these days! Among their wide remit is dealing with chemical and biological terrorism and explosions. Their experts were at the scenes of the London Tube and bus bombings in 2005 as well being involved with retrieval and analysis of evidence that assisted in the prosecutions that followed. DSTL scientists test the likelihood of success of home-made bombs. If they're doing this work and someone charged with terrorism offences wants to challenge the science, then independent scientists like my colleagues and me are required.

I know a man who spends his time, among other things, training ex-soldiers in bomb detection. A company with which I regularly work has recently acquired a cadaver dog (a dog that detects cadavers, not a dog that is itself a cadaver). I love helping them out with training courses because it's so very interesting and entertaining. The people who attend the training courses are police officers, crime scene examiners, crime scene managers and forensic pathologists. Between them, they've seen every type of scene imaginable. One of the other course presenters has spent time in Eastern Europe and the Middle East examining war crimes and blood spatter patterns — not the sorts of stories that are ever casually recounted over dinner but an account of such a crime scene is entirely appropriate at an outdoor body recovery course. It's those sorts of stories that make me realise how far-reaching our work can be and why I enjoy being part of the training course; I always feel as though I've learnt as much as I've taught.

One thing that has resulted from TV programmes like *CSI* is an enormous interest in forensic science, because people think the job of a forensic scientist is as glamorous as it is portrayed on the screen. Not so. Sometimes it's extremely boring and it doesn't usually involve high speed car chases or being shot at. Scientists who work in more traditional roles for criminal prosecution laboratories can be quite restricted in what they do. A scientist who did a degree in chemistry might get a job in the drugs section of a prosecution laboratory, which means that for the indeterminable future they'll be opening evidence bags that usually, but not always, contain drugs. They'll apply the standard set of protocols (describe what you see, weigh it, analyse it using standard methods or send it to someone who will do the analysis and send you the results), write a report, move on to the next case. The chances of someone in the drugs section (other than those doing analysis of clandestine drug laboratories) giving evidence is, in my experience anyway, much lower than working in other areas of forensic science. Let's face it, there's usually not much to argue about when it comes to identification of 10 kilograms of cocaine.

Biology graduates usually end up in the biology/DNA section where they'll process items and samples in a case then move right on to the next case. The main difference for DNA scientists is that they work in what are described as 'clean environments', which means they're constantly changing lab coats, face masks, gloves, overshoes, trousers … it's a hugely wasteful industry in terms of the non-recyclable items, which are chucked out on a daily basis.

Most of what I do as an independent expert involves examining scientific reports. Again, that sounds incredibly boring. *Au contraire*: a scientific report that lands on a lawyer's desk is, metaphorically, exactly like an onion. From a distance, it usually looks lovely and has a smooth-looking exterior. As we all know, onions are made up of many layers, just like a scientific report. Each layer took time to grow, each of the layers supporting the overlying layer. At the centre of the onion lies the original item that led to the preparation of the report.

Just like a real onion, it's not until you pick up a report and have a good grapple with it that you can make an assessment of whether it's good and solid or whether the skin's going to crumple at the slightest pressure. That's where I come in — as the onion specialist. A lot of lawyers look at the onion on the desk and try to pick holes in the outer surface without actually picking it up and seeing what's gone into making the onion the size it is. My advice is that when you've got an onion on your desk, get an onion specialist to take a good, sharp knife and cut through it to see what's inside. If there are bad layers under there, everything over the top of it might be tainted and need throwing out.

Like the best onions, some scientific reports have few layers, are small, sweet and very good. Others, on the other hand, are large, multi-layered monstrosities that took a long time to grow and when you cut into them, they make your eyes water. Although many lawyers don't like to examine science too carefully in case they don't like what they'll find, in many cases it's possible to examine it without compromising anyone's legal position. I just always think that it's at least worth having a quick look to see whether you've got a good or bad onion.

While I know about lots of different sorts of metaphorical onions, real ones aren't my forté — people who know me know that cooking is not one of my strengths. However, my areas of scientific/onion expertise are diverse and varied, purely because of my background and training. It means my day job is far more fun because I like the unexpected — you never know what's going to arrive in the post. Like the day a pair of soiled knickers fell out of an envelope onto the desk — a very unexpected onion indeed. Luckily, it wasn't my desk. No, it was one of our personal assistants. She basically did all the non-scientific stuff in the office, including opening the post.

On this particular day, she slit the envelope with the letter knife and — plop — out they fell! A pair of pale pink, soiled knickers, with a small note and a business card. It seemed that someone, somewhere, had been cheating on her husband, who was a lawyer. He picked up what he deemed to be an offending set of underwear, stuck them in an envelope with a disgruntled note and sent them off to us for 'analysis'. The problem with that sort of approach is that there are all kinds of issues about continuity of the item, accidental contamination of the DNA because of handling by our unfortunate PA and anything the knickers might have soaked up on their way through the postal system. After all, it was a cold, wet, winter's day, the envelope had been wet and the knickers were without any packaging save for said soggy envelope. Even if we did get a DNA result, what were we supposed to do with it? Without a reference sample from the disgruntled husband, we couldn't interpret the results.

Despite a few carefully worded messages left on the business card's phone number (one has to be careful with message wording — one never knows who might be checking voicemails), we never heard a single thing. That in itself leaves a problem. We now have a pair of ownerless knickers sitting in the office. We can't destroy them because they might be required as evidence. We can't get hold of the owner or the client because there's no answer on the phone or to our letters. What happens? In that case, I have no idea. As far as I know, those pink frillies are still in the office.

Independent expert witnesses are nothing without solicitors and barristers. Without them, we don't get any work. We rely on receiving full and accurate information from them because our work can only ever be as good as the information with which we are provided. As the old sayings go, *rubbish in, rubbish out, you can't make a silk purse out of a sow's ear* and *it's quality, not quantity, that matters.* We receive our instructions usually in the form of letters because this is the legal arena and everything should be documented and recorded. It's important to remember at this point that lawyers have to act on their clients' instructions, no matter what the lawyer thinks about those instructions. Lawyers can advise their clients but the client doesn't have to take that advice.

It's always amusing when we receive bizarre instructions, which sometimes we don't understand, and even the solicitors don't understand. Take this letter we received in a drink-driving case, which included the phrase: *To the line and also lies showed a lower reading of H2.* Now, I know a fair bit about drink-driving cases but I had not the faintest idea what this was all about. After having read through the file, though, I could see where the problem had arisen. The breath-testing device that had been used was the Lion Intoxilyzer and the results of the two breath samples were 84 and 82. The sentence should have read, *The Lion Intoxilyzer showed a lower reading of 82.* When I rang the solicitor and read it to him, he said we had passed the test and he was just keeping us on our toes (and that he had a new secretary who'd never done legal work before and had never heard of a Lion Intoxilyzer).

Then there are the instructions that are in the sort of code the police use for describing events. In this particular case, a defendant had crashed into a street sign when he *failed to adequately negotiate a bend.* We were advised that, fortunately, neither the driver nor passenger was injured, although the driver somehow managed to acquire a head wound when diving into a bush in an attempt to evade capture by the police. I was intrigued, and went on to read the full, bizarre series of events. The police described chasing the driver, on foot by this time, until they came to a corner. *As I rounded the corner, my colleague was partially blocking my view but I became aware of a pair of legs sticking out of the bush which we made a move to grab hold of.* As it turns out, the driver had panicked and jumped into the nearest bush when he was out of sight of the police. Unfortunately, it was a laurel bush and was very sturdy, so sturdy in fact that he couldn't get into it properly and couldn't get out of it again either. Luckily for him, the Boys in Blue were close by to give him a helping hand.

Sometimes, solicitors have to admit that their clients might have been a bit naughty. One solicitor wrote to advise that his client admitted that, at some point, he was obstructive to the police and there was an altercation between the client and the police officers. The general tone of the letter was something like: *The defendant was eventually conveyed to the police station, having first attended hospital to receive treatment for a head injury.* There was no indication in the letter of how the defendant acquired the head injury but the police officer's statement was quite telling. *The defendant began to remove his watch to allow me to apply the handcuffs. He placed his watch down on a kitchen counter and then pulled out a carving knife from the kitchen drawer and raised it above his head in a threatening manner.* I have to ask if there is any other way to hold a knife above your head in front of two police officers without it looking threatening. It seems that the defendant was eventually disarmed with a few blasts of pepper spray and a clonk on the head with a police-issue baton.

Another case involved a defendant who denied consuming excessive quantities of alcohol in a drink-driving case. The defendant said that a man she didn't know bought her four drinks of lemonade and that he must have spiked her drinks heavily with vodka, although she didn't notice at the time. She agreed her car may have been swerving but this was due to thick fog. Did she mean the fog was driving her car?

Yet another defendant proffered that although she was six times over the legal breath alcohol level and had been found slumped over the steering wheel of her car surrounded by several empty vodka bottles, surely the breath test result must have been wrong.

Then there was the man who was facing an assault charge. *I accept presence and participation in the altercation. The reason the forensic evidence suggests I was there is because I was there and involved in the incident.* As far as it goes, that has to be about as helpful as a defendant's statement can get.

Sometimes, the statements are just not particularly clear. For example: *I noted that he had matted blood about his hair on all sides. He was bald.*

Whether a case requires a formal written statement, a report or a brief letter, it's critical to convey on paper the things I consider to be important in any given case. This is my only chance to transfer my opinion about this case to the person who instructed me. Experience, and many lawyers, have also taught me that a lot of people just read the last section of any report, usually the one headed Summary/Conclusions.

Just as you were taught at junior school when you were seven, it's very important to write a story with a beginning, middle and an end. Take it a step further to when you were about 13 and writing up your first proper science experiments. The voice of your teacher echoing out of the classroom as you all charge out, like Pamplona bulls, after the bell rings on Friday afternoon: 'Everyone remember to write Introduction, Methods, Results and Conclusions.' Skip forward to your last year before leaving school — exams. The one thing every teacher says a million times is ANSWER THE QUESTION. You won't get marks for waffle and padding. A whole wash of Teachers Past has just swum through my brain, all repeating the same thing ...

Science writing at the forensic level is no different. Reports should be written so they can be read in isolation and the reader can follow what's happening. It's no use yabbering on about photograph 73 if no one else can see it.

Every report, statement, letter or document that leaves the office must be prepared with the thought that it might be used against you at some point — not necessarily by your instructing party but by anyone to whom your communication has been provided. Every telephone conversation, email or text you send is available for repeat and, possibly, inaccurate repetition, probably in your absence. Never mind that in the United Kingdom, New Zealand, Australia and other places the rights the police read to the suspect cum defendant say something along the lines of: *You have the right to remain silent. Anything you do or say may be used in evidence.* What should happen is that when you train as an expert witness you should have your *lack* of rights read to you: *Anything you write, say or do as an expert witness may and probably will be used against you, probably when you're in the witness box and probably when you least expect it.* If you write a report or statement or letter or email, whatever, if it doesn't feel right, don't send it. Better it be a day late than chase you around the appeal courts and haunt your nightmares for the next 10 years.

If you end up having to read your report out in court, which is usually tediously boring for all concerned, it has to be understandable by a layperson, as well as convey all the important scientific points you want to make. Regardless of who's giving evidence, it's not fun watching the eyes of the jury glaze over … who's going to be first to nod off? That bloke in the corner on the back row? Surely not the one in the front row — everyone can see him?

I think one of the main things I've learnt over the years is that my role as a forensic scientist is as a science communicator. It's probably the single biggest difference between academic scientists and forensic scientists. For academics, using as many technical phrases as possible in a scientific journal is very important because it demonstrates not only an understanding of the academic aspects of their field of expertise, it means it takes fewer words to write a description, which is important when only 250 words are available for an abstract. Academics are usually sparring with their peers and fighting for funding. Forensic scientists have a different audience — we just try to explain what is sometimes a complicated scientific issue as simply as possible. Some are better at it than others.

Chapter 4

The *CSI* effect

Forensic scientists soon discover when talking to the general public that many people have an extremely limited knowlege of forensic science and the tasks it performs. As conversations continue it becomes apparent that misconstrued ideas often originate from watching television dramas.

Caddy and Cobb in White, 2004

This is the big misconception so I'm going to deal with this face on, at the start, just to get it out of the way and cleared up. What is forensic science? That's easy — it's what you see on *CSI*, isn't it? It's just like it is on *Bones* and *NCIS* (or 'knickers' as we say in our house) and all those other American crime TV series.

If only it were that simple and, let's face it, glamorous. I'd love to have a laboratory like theirs, with all that moody lighting and shiny shelving. In practice, the shelves they have on *CSI: Las Vegas* would be a contamination nightmare — all those nooks and crannies. Yes, I know, you've probably never even noticed the shelves in Grissom's lab — have a look when the next re-runs are on. They seem to work in a perpetual state of semi-darkness, which entailed Grissom getting a torch out in a mortuary on one occasion because he and the pathologist couldn't see what they were doing. You'd think they'd go for the main light or have one of those torches they used to have on *The X-Files* that could light up half a state at the flick of a switch.

I'd love to have the budget they have for their work clothes as well. Have you seen the way they swank around crime scenes, not a face mask or coverall suit in sight? Astounding. Designer gear, high-heeled boots, designer sunglasses. Their cars are pretty cool too — great big four-wheel-drive things or flash saloons with comfy seats. Not the sorts of vehicles that have had stinky body parts packed in cool boxes in the boot, smelly overalls plonked in the back because some human putrefaction juice got onto them by mistake or wellies/gumboots (depending on your country of origin) for wearing at clandestine methamphetamine laboratories. In my experience, attendance at a crime scene generally involves dressing head to foot in a giant plastic bag, wearing surgical gloves and a face mask. Sometimes, you have to wear gloves for so long your skin looks as if you've been in the bath for several hours. If only five hours processing pollen samples in the heat of summer in a laboratory were as pleasurable as a lie in the bath with a good book: same skin appearance, different way of achieving it.

Grissom et al. also have a terribly inappropriate habit of clambering through a crime scene, finding a piece of 'something' seemingly innocuous (but later found to be crucial) and picking it up from amid the debris, sometimes with a pen but sometimes just with fingers — *before* said item has been photographed *in situ*. Rule number 1 at a crime scene: Observe and record. DO NOT TOUCH. Once the item has been moved, even accidentally, its evidential value is shattered, potentially rendering any results obtained from it meaningless.

I can't ever recall *CSI* agents putting items into evidence bags either. Where's the officer in charge of exhibits who's receiving all these items from everyone at the scene, logging the details on a datasheet so everyone knows what is in the item, the evidence bag's unique number, who found it, where, what time and date and what happened to it after it was collected? A crime scene should be a controlled environment. It's simply not appropriate for 16 people to wander through a crime scene before the videoing, photography and all the items of interest have been recorded.

Once identified as a crime scene (and that includes bodies as well as the places they were found), the crime scene should be controlled and everyone entering and leaving should be monitored and their arrival/departure recorded.

As I understand it, there was good crime scene control in 1996, in a well-known New Zealand case, the Tania Furlan murder. I remember that day clear as a bell because I was with Tania Furlan's husband when he received the call at work to say she had been attacked and his baby daughter had been taken.

In the Furlan case, because the police knew who had entered and left the scene in the time after Tania had been found and the scene had been controlled, they were able to examine the soles of the footwear of all those people who had come and gone. The sole patterns were compared with sole patterns found in the hallway of the house and every set of sole patterns could be attributed to a legitimate person's shoes — except one, which told the police they probably belonged to a *person of interest*. For those who aren't familiar with the case, the baby was later found safe and well but abandoned outside a church in Auckland. No one was convicted of Tania's murder because the suspect committed suicide while on remand in Auckland's Mt Eden Prison before the trial began — just one aspect of a controversial case.

As mentioned previously, crime scenes should be recorded and documented (photographs, plans, maps, notes, diagrams, photographs, videos) before items are appropriately moved and removed. After that, a long chain of events occurs, every step of which should be recorded. The idea is that anyone can come along at a later date and see exactly what happened to which item at what time/date and what that meant for the eventual outcome of the case. I've worked on a couple of thousand of cases and being able to follow a particular item from crime scene to police station to laboratory via the paper trail is absolutely vital. If I can't track it, how can anyone else know what happened to it? Remember that some of these cases take years to be resolved.

The David Bain case is an obvious example. That started way back in 1994 and there were significant difficulties in court when people were asked what had happened to items in the interim — after all, who can accurately remember what happened to an item they found or handled all the way back then if they haven't written it down?

So strong is the influence of TV that the forensic science community recognises what is referred to as the *CSI effect*.

Basically, people, including lawyers, expect science to answer crimes in the way it does on *CSI*. Perhaps not in an hour (including commercial breaks) but certainly far more quickly than is realistic and also far more neatly than is actually possible. *CSI* and similar programmes generally end very neatly, with no loose ends, whereas in reality there are often unexplained things that remain that way, even where people plead guilty.

I've been working in forensic science since 1998 and it is just so far from *CSI* that I feel compelled to shout at the TV every time I watch an episode of *CSI* (all locations), *Bones, NCIS* and, sometimes, *The Bill*. So why do I watch them? Because I like 'em. Lawyers shout at *Law & Order, SVU* and *Coronation Street*, geologists shout at *Dante's Peak, Jurassic Park* and *One Million Years B.C.*, medics shout at *Holby City, Casualty, Shortland Street* and, I assume, *ER* (because it can't be perfect, surely).

What amazes me is not that the TV viewing public is taken in by these programmes, because I think this surely must only apply to a relatively small number of individuals, but that the *CSI* effect didn't occur earlier. There's never been any suggestion of a *Murder She Wrote* effect or a *Poirot* effect or even a *Magnum, P.I.* effect. Sadly, though, I must report that I have experienced the *CSI* effect, and not just from the general public, but also from lawyers.

Here is an extract from IrishTimes.com (19 August 2009, article by Bernice Harrison):

It's thanks to CSI that millions of us fancy ourselves as forensics experts. DNA profiling, blood spatter patterns, latent prints — who couldn't throw a bit of forensic banter into a conversation and, after nine years of the mega-hit TV series, there can't be many viewers who wouldn't be quietly confident of nabbing the baddie if let loose on a crime scene.

Unusually for a science-based programme, it's glamorous, too. Every week — and without a thought for scene contamination (see, we're all experts) — forensic investigator Catherine Willows swishes her fabulous red hair over dead bodies, dropping follicles into crucial evidence as she goes and Nick Stokes, her beefcake sidekick, wouldn't be seen dead in one of those deeply unflattering one-piece paper suits worn by crime scene guys in the real world. But who cares, when even the trickiest murder is solved at the end of the programme? It's not so popular in court rooms, however; a phenomenon called 'the CSI effect' has been wryly noted, whereby CSI-savvy jurors have an unreasonably high expectation of what forensic evidence can prove. After all, if slightly creepy CSI boss Gil Grissom and his team can work their science magic, week in, week out, on the murdered in Las Vegas, surely it can't be that difficult.

Indeed.

I recall being asked by instructing defence counsel at court in England a few years ago if my job was like *CSI*. To be honest, I was a bit surprised to hear him ask this question (and he was serious), given that I was attending some dingy magistrates' court for a recidivist drink driver and also given that he was a criminal law specialist. I shouldn't be surprised because it's still by far the most commonly asked question I hear. I usually just answer, 'Yes, but with less lipstick, fewer dead bodies and more paperwork ...'

❀

I gave a lecture recently about forensic science in the United Kingdom and what a great place it is to get work experience, which is very true. However, it's hard not to be negative about a career in forensic science because there have been so many redundancies (800 in England and Wales) and police budgets are being cut in both New Zealand and the United Kingdom. In my mind, based on my experience, I believe this is inevitably setting someone up for a miscarriage of justice. Not long afterwards, I read an article in the Guardian Online which confirmed my worst fears. It reported that the United Kingdom Forensic Science Service currently has 1300 scientists, and went on to say that the United Kingdom's largest private provider, LGC Forensics, employs 500 people. In 1990 there were just two forensic science degree courses in the United Kingdom. In 2008, 1667 students embarked on a total of 285 such courses. This massive increase in numbers is largely attributed to the *CSI* effect. I like the final sentence in the article: *in order to ensure there are enough jobs to go round, more than half of them will have to retrain as serial killers.* And what better people to know how to cover their tracks than forensic scientists?

Real-life research has been undertaken to assess the impact of effects of programmes like *CSI, Bones* and *Law & Order.* These programmes do affect people's perceptions. Maybe it's because they want to believe real life can be that exciting. Perhaps it's also a security thing — if something bad happened in their lives, science can rush to the rescue and solve the crime. I've had it put to me that even if the cases on *CSI* aren't always believable, the methods applied surely must be correct. Isn't it right that if a footwear mark is found at a crime scene, the police can use the sole pattern to identify the brand, barcode number, number of pairs made, location of manufacture and date of import? In a word, no.

Few cases involve more than one or two types of science. Many cases, even criminal cases, have no scientific content whatsoever. Most of the cases in which I have been involved usually had one evidence type, sometimes two — three or more can get very complicated. Multi-evidence cases more often than not involve DNA plus something else — most prosecutors have wisely decided never to bring a prosecution solely on DNA findings. It's interesting that in some US states, when juries are being selected, potential jurors are asked about what they watch on TV.

There are two other things to consider regarding the *CSI* effect. The first is speed and turnaround times. Not only is the expectation that science will provide full and complete answers, but also that it can be done quickly and on every occasion. Unfortunately, it's not like *CSI* where a sample can be placed into a machine and an answer pops out after five minutes. Some analyses take what appear to be a long time. Processing of samples sometimes only takes a few hours but consideration has to be given not just to the results but also the interpretation. Thinking time has to be built into the reporting system. What seems like an unsolvable question today might easily be answered in two days' time, probably at two in the morning when one is half asleep.

The other factor is that of case limitations. Science is evolving at a rapid pace and, in the long run, will probably achieve anything people want — it's the age-old story that if the human mind can imagine it, it will probably eventuate, even if it's in 200 years' time. However, in legal casework it is important to remember that the limitations of each case are the main restricting factors affecting the application of science, not the science itself. Just because DNA didn't work in a particular case doesn't mean it won't work next time; it just means that for this particular case insufficient DNA was present for a profile to be obtained. Even if a DNA profile was obtained from a crime scene, it doesn't necessarily follow that the owner of the DNA perpetrated the crime.

Many top-level scientists agree that the *CSI* effect exists and it affects how people view them. Bob Shaler was the man charged with handling DNA identification after the World Trade Centre bombings, so he knows his stuff. It's disappointing for many when he says, 'I was a crime lab guy, but I was never the person portrayed on TV. That person doesn't really exist.'

The *CSI* effect has also been felt as far as organisations like the United Nations, which is involved with what is referred to as 'wildlife forensics'. This is the branch of forensic science applied to issues around poaching, import/export of rare, exotic and controlled species. It's a fascinating area of science. The UN is looking to adopt a forensic science approach to assist in managing the problems of illegal fishing. At a UN Food and Agriculture Organization workshop in Rome in 2010 they discussed what techniques could assist and how. As usual, DNA analysis was at the fore, probably for a combination of reasons: it's very well known and it has huge application. DNA analysis can be used to identify fish species, which in turn can answer the question of whether it's a species that shouldn't be fished. Chemical analyses are also applicable in wildlife forensics for testing bones and other items to identify what nutrients were absorbed by the creature when it was alive and therefore from where they were caught, which can determine if the catch came from a restricted area. I always say that there is no end to the types of casework to which a forensic science approach can be applied and this is a perfect example. Particularly given that one participant at the UN meeting described how a group convicted of illegally trading abalone confessed to learning how to destroy evidence by watching *CSI: Miami.*

Just as an aside, and following on with the wildlife DNA theme, a sign that this is an expanding area of forensic science is when sessions specialising in wildlife forensics are included in conferences such as the 2010 Australia and New Zealand Forensic Science Society 20th International Symposium in Sydney.

Wolves have been a protected species in Europe for some time, and since the 1970s, have been protected in Italy. A number of wolves were found killed and sometimes mutilated (the muzzle missing from at least one) in the Genoa region. A man was eventually arrested and a necklace of teeth in his possession was seized. The teeth were sent to the Italian Institute for Environmental Protection and Research (ISPRA) where wildlife specialists extracted DNA. As with any case like this, unless there is a database against which to compare results, the results themselves are more or less meaningless. However, there is in fact a DNA database for wolves and other large predators, used to assist with population monitoring. The DNA is gathered from many sources including cadavers and faecal matter (not forgetting other possible sources such as fur, skin, bones). Six separate wolves were identified from the necklace using the DNA database. Obviously, not all killers wear their victims' teeth, but keeping mementos of hunting is not at all unusual and it makes perfect sense to use trophy items to attempt to link a possible offender with an offence.

Just to finish my ranting about the *CSI* effect, it was very gratifying to hear one of the world's foremost DNA scientists and pioneers of DNA in forensics, Dr Peter Gill, say exactly the same thing, specifically about DNA. Dr Gill's general sentiment was that *CSI* and similar programmes don't really represent the way in which forensic science works in the real world. Programmes like those give the impression that if a DNA profile is recovered from a crime scene and you have a suspect then it must be the suspect who committed the crime. It doesn't necessarily follow that a suspect is guilty of that crime because there are so many other things which have to be considered. Forensic scientists shouldn't necessarily just report (or review) the science in isolation — the framework into which that science fits is crucial for the proper under-standing of what the science is telling the trier of fact (usually a jury and/or a judge). It is then for the trier of fact to decide what weight to apply to that evidence when deciding on the ultimate issue, which is usually down to two choices: guilty or not guilty.

Forensic science can, of course, also be used for investigative purposes — and it may take an investigation down a different track from the one the investigators were expecting. The important thing is that the investigators should take that scientific information into account when deciding what to do next — just sticking with their previous track of thought may be neither appropriate nor correct.

My favourite quote from Dr Gill is: 'The scientist is not there to prosecute anyone. Whether the individual is found guilty or innocent has no bearing on the science.' Dr Gill makes an extremely valid point. All forensic scientists should be impartial and unbiased in their reporting — with no exceptions.

Chapter 5

Forensic science breakdown

Discussing forensic science in theory is one thing, knowing how that applies in the real world is entirely different and not at all like *CSI*. It's the same with any subject: you can read as much as you like in books and scientific journals but the time you *really* understand it is when you actually do it for the first time, hands on. The next best thing is to learn from case studies, particularly for people who are interested in forensic science but not necessarily wanting to do it for a living, such as the sorts of people whom I assume will be reading this book.

Scientific theory and research do, of course, have their places in forensic science. Ongoing research is the stuff that moves the science forwards which, in turn, allows more and more areas of science to be presented as evidence in court. Without research, forensic science would become stuck in the proverbial rut. It's also important to refine techniques that have already been developed just so that we can ensure the methods being used are up to the job or are replaced with something quicker, more reliable and cheaper, much to the bean-counters' delight. All forensic laboratories run on tight budgets so the cheaper a technique becomes, the more samples can be tested or the more testing that can be applied in any given case, which generally leads to more questions being answered and a greater chance of arrest, charge and successful prosecution of the correct people.

An example would be development of a new technique to collect pollen from the nasal passages of deceased people. The old method involved several people for several hours in a mortuary waiting for the opportune moment to roll a body and wash out the nasal passages; the new technique involves a few minutes, a lidded test tube and a brush. Much cheaper, quicker and therefore much more likely to be used. Another example is recently completed research that looked at how knives cut through clothing that is well worn (as opposed to new fabric). A simple bit of work but it will help deal with those difficult questions a sharp barrister might ask about the differences between stab tests being undertaken on a new pair of jeans instead of jeans that had been worn for months, like the ones forming the exhibit in a case.

The successful conclusion of a case often lies in how much money can be spent on it, not on the limitations of science or police ability — an uncomfortable truth but that's the reality of modern day police work and forensic science. Many people will consider that it isn't ethical or right for modern society to place a monetary value on crime investigation, but like it or not, that's just how it is; same as it is in the health services, hospitals, child protection services, fire services, refuse collection, in fact all publicly funded organisations. When I worked in England, there was a seasonal lag in drug trace cases in the second quarter of the year because the police budget had run out and the new one didn't kick in until April.

If we take a crime such as murder by gunshot, the number

of personnel involved is enormous — and all of them have to be paid: initial police attending the scene, ambulance crew, pathologist plus mortuary assistant(s) to conduct the post-mortem, police officers involved with the case with some-times several officers in charge of the crime scene if it's a large one, with one officer per body and an exhibits officer to coordinate item collection, logging, tracking, several crime scene examiners, fingerprint examiner(s), ballistics expert(s) and toxicologists to analyse and interpret results from blood and other body samples.

Then there's the cost of scene equipment, with disposable items such as scene suits, bootees, gloves, face masks, chemicals, evidence bags, transfer of the body to mortuary, hospital costs, sample analysis costs, courier or transfer costs (exhibits and items from scenes have to be transported by secure means in order to ensure continuity of the item and continuous chain of custody) — the list rolls on, even before we get to the cost of legal services, the courts, judges, etc. It's all a hugely complicated, money-spending machine that is vital in order for you and me to sit at home and feel a modicum of safety.

What I plan to do in this chapter is briefly discuss why we bother to examine the science at all, what makes an expert an expert in what they do and why it's important that an appropriate expert is instructed.

Purely for argument's sake, let's say there's such a thing as a straightforward murder case. While I've never had the experience of working with such a case, it should be pretty obvious that shooting another person in the heart is generally going to result in the heart owner's death — we can all understand that. Why then would we bother to examine the science?

Well, sometimes questions arise from this sort of death such as how far away would the shooter have been to cause that injury; could Weapon A have caused that injury; how quickly would the deceased have died? All these questions have an impact on determining the circumstances of the death, which is crucial to understanding what happened and who, if anyone, was to blame or was at fault. So back to the original observation that everyone knows shooting another person in the heart usually results in death — while we know what happened on a superficial level, it requires an expert to talk about the detailed mechanics of what *exactly* happened, which often tellingly includes *how* and *when* it happened.

In the circumstances of our straightforward murder we'd need a ballistics expert to talk about the firearm, firearms discharge residue and projectile trajectory, a pathologist and/or medic to talk about wound geometry and speed of death, and maybe a blood pattern analyst to talk about relative locations of people and items at the time of the events. That's on top of the usual analyses such as DNA of any blood spatter recovered from moving items (such as a person who ran away after firing the fatal shot) or toxicology to determine whether the deceased was drunk, affected by drugs or toxins, or was taking medication at the time of their death.

If we don't examine these issues then we can't be sure of what happened, particularly if there's no one left alive to tell us. Even if anyone is still alive, there's no guarantee that they'd want to tell the police the truth about what happened. What we're left with is what we can see, measure and collect and sometimes, even more importantly, what we can't see but can still collect, measure, investigate and magnify. To borrow from *CSI* and Grissom for a change, these are the silent witnesses that were present and can tell us about what happened without uttering a word.

After the David Bain retrial had finished on 5 June 2009, there was a line in the Christchurch *Press* newspaper that really perplexed me. It read, *Every piece of Crown evidence was put under the microscope [by the defence] in a way possibly never seen before in New Zealand.* My first reaction to this was *what?* How can it possibly be that in a country like New Zealand, which has its judicial roots in the same system I grew up in, the media thinks examination by the defence of the evidence being put forward by the Crown is in some way an exceptional situation?

Either the media has no idea what happens in courtrooms, which cannot be the case because some of these reporters are *court* reporters, or the media genuinely had never before seen anything like the investigation undertaken by Bain's defence team. Well, I for one don't want to believe that and I'm sure no one else wants to believe it either — how can there be any trust in a justice system that doesn't robustly challenge what is being presented?

Best case scenario is that the media was sensationalising what it had observed. Worst case scenario is that the statement is true. If it's the latter then there is clearly a whole lot of work that should be done in casework that currently isn't being done.

Having established that even simple circumstances can be assisted by science, the question then asked is why instruct an expert? Why can't information just be put before the court for the court to decide what it means?

Although the trier of fact knows that to shoot someone in the heart is probably fatal, they often require assistance with information that falls outside what could be called 'common knowledge'. Experts give the court advice, in the form of evidence, on issues that don't fall within the court's ordinary knowledge or experience. That usually means an expert has had some form of special training or study.

For the areas of information that require specialist knowledge, the police have an on-tap pool of expertise into which to dip its toes, or jump in wholeheartedly. In New Zealand, it has ESR Forensic. In England and Wales there is a bit more of a choice because of the larger population size. There police forensic work is put up for tender and there's a big scrap over which organisation gets what. There are 43 regional police forces plus the British Transport police, each requiring forensic science services. Some forces choose to do the work in-house, some farm all of it out, some do a combination. Fingerprint work, for example, has traditionally always been done in-house as has road traffic incident investigations (crashes to you and me). The Forensic Science Service is the equivalent of ESR Forensic, in that it used to be run directly by the government but is now run as a separate business unit. There are other organisations such as LGC (Laboratory of the Government Chemist) that was privatised and became such a significant player that it was able to take over another independent laboratory, Forensic Alliance. Between them, the FSS and LGC hold the majority of the police contracts but things have changed recently, with more and more tender work being won by smaller service providers.

But what about the independent sector? People need independent sample analysis — blood alcohol samples, DNA samples, glass analyses, drug sample analysis, urine samples from prisoners (because they're not supposed to be taking drugs in prison, you know). England and Wales have several smaller independent laboratories undertaking this kind of work but New Zealand struggles somewhat in this department because of its population size. This means that people like me spend time arranging for samples to be sent overseas to be analysed.

Back to the original question now: why is there any need to employ an independent expert? It comes down to basics: an independent quality control check. When I present lectures on this topic, there are six cases to which I refer. As with New Zealand, England and Wales has its fair share of problems when it comes to forensic science and there are unfortunately several other cases to which I could refer, but those below are the least technical and the most demonstrative. There are of course several high-profile New Zealand cases that could be used as examples but I intend sticking to English cases because people get tied up with the emotional aspects, which cloud the importance of the science. Emotions and science don't mix so in New Zealand I talk about English cases and, in England, I talk about New Zealand cases.

Angela Cannings and Sally Clark

In 1989, Angela Cannings' baby died at the age of 13 weeks. Another seven-week-old son died in 1991 and in 1999 her 18-week-old son died. After the first death, the view seemed to be that this was unfortunate — poor lady. The subsequent deaths were viewed as something else and more than just coincidence — how could a woman have more than one baby die as the result of natural causes? She was charged with murder, tried and convicted.

Sally Clark gave birth to a boy in 1996 but he was found dead in his Moses basket at 11 weeks of age. Death was certified as 'natural causes'. She later had another boy in 1997 who, eight weeks later, suddenly collapsed. The parents requested a specialist pathological examination, as did the hospital paediatrician. Unfortunately, this did not occur and the post-mortem was performed by the local Home Office pathologist. After four weeks' delay, the parents were arrested. The pathologist had reported retina and brain damage attributed to 'baby shaking'. Review of the first child's death resulted in the original certification of natural causes being replaced with smothering. In July 1998 Sally Clark was charged with the murder of both babies. An expert paediatrician for the prosecution said during the trial that the chance of a double cot death in the Clark family, at one in 73 million, was 'vanishingly small'. However, it was accepted by both the Crown and the defence that there was no evidence both babies died of cot death. The same expert witness gave evidence in the trial of Angela Cannings. Crown evidence was that Mrs Cannings had smothered her children.

Figures from the Care of Next Infant (CONI) charity are that one cot death occurs in every 8500 babies, but after one cot death the risk of a second actually increases to one in 200. The statistic of 1:73 million quoted by the expert in the Sally Clark case is five times smaller than the chance of winning the English lottery.

The Royal Statistical Society issued a statement in 2001 (News Release, Tuesday 23 October 2001), prompted by issues raised by the Sally Clark case, expressing its concern at the misuse of statistics in the courts:

> *In the recent highly publicised case of R v Sally Clark, a medical expert witness drew on published studies to obtain a figure for the frequency of sudden infant death syndrome (SIDS) in families having some of the characteristics of the defendant's family. He went on to square this figure to obtain a value of 1 in 73 million for the frequency of two cases of SIDS in such a family.*
>
> *This approach is, in general, statistically invalid. The well-publicised figure of 1 in 73 million … has no statistical basis.*

After many battles, both women had their convictions quashed and were released from prison, Sally Clark in 2003 after three years in prison (she died in 2007, aged 42), and Angela Cannings in 2004, after 20 months in prison. In the review of Angela Cannings' case, the court was told the paediatrician's evidence was misleading and, in future, his testimony would need a 'health warning' attached to it. A BBC investigation showed that on her father's side, Mrs Cannings' grandmother had lost one child to cot death and her great-grandmother had lost two.

The paediatric expert witness was eventually struck off in 2005 but was later reinstated. The original pathologist in the Clark case was found guilty of serious professional misconduct.

The Birmingham Six

The Birmingham Six (never let it be said that the British media is short of catchy tag lines) were six men sentenced to life imprisonment in 1975 after being tried and convicted of the 1974 series of pub bombings in Birmingham, central England. Twenty-one people were killed and 162 were injured in the two coordinated bomb blasts, which were separated by two minutes.

A prosecution forensic scientist used a positive result from a screening test to claim a 99 per cent certainty that two of the defendants had handled explosives. The test results were opposed by a prominent defence expert. The test used is not conclusive and, over time, proved to have limited value; the test has not been used by the British police forces since the mid-1980s.

The case was far more complicated than this brief summary, but the convictions were declared unsafe and overturned in 1991 by the Court of Appeal. At the appeal, evidence was presented regarding fabrication and suppression of evidence by the police and the forensic evidence was discredited. This led to the Crown withdrawing most of its case against the men. The Court of Appeal stated that the conclusion of the forensic scientist '... was wrong, and demonstrably wrong, judged even by the state of forensic science in 1974'.

Damilola Taylor

Damilola Taylor was a 10-year-old boy who died in November 2000 as the result of a single stab wound to his left leg, while on his way home from a library in South London. Numerous items were seized from several suspects by the police and examined by a major forensic science laboratory. Several youths were arrested; four were charged with Damilola Taylor's murder. While they were subsequently cleared in April 2002, after their acquittals the police reinvestigated the case and sent all items seized to a different forensic science laboratory. Scientists at the second laboratory found traces of Damilola's blood on a training shoe worn by one of the arrested youths and on the cuff of a jumper belonging to another. Fibres within the stain found on the training shoe were indistinguishable from those in Damilola's trousers. The first examination of the shoe had been undertaken by an Assistant Scientific Officer (ASO). The ASO's work had been reviewed by the scientist who eventually reported the case, but the reporting scientist didn't actually examine the shoe themselves, apparently because of a lack of time. As a result of this case, forensic organisations tightened up their examination and review procedures. Reporting officers must now examine the items themselves, although this is done after the main examination has been done by an ASO. While police eventually achieved manslaughter convictions in 2006 for two youths, who were aged 12 and 13 at the time of Damilola's death, there was significant criticism not only of the way the forensic science was handled but also of the way the case was investigated by the police.

Omagh bombing

In August 1988, a paramilitary car bomb went off in Omagh, County Tyrone, Northern Ireland. Twenty-nine people died and approximately 220 people were injured. The attack was carried out by the Real Irish Republican Army (RIRA), who later claimed responsibility.

The person most recently charged with the attack was

Sean Hoey. A significant part of the Crown case relied upon the results of low copy number (LCN) DNA analysis linking Mr Hoey with several bombs. However, during the trial an alleged leading authority on LCN DNA indicated that the technique wasn't up to muster and in late 2007 the case against Mr Hoey collapsed.

As a result, the Crown Prosecution Service (CPS) in England and Wales briefly suspended the use of the technique in early 2008 and all cases going through the courts in which LCN DNA findings formed part of the case were reviewed. Although the CPS never said how many cases were involved, the Forensic Science Service had used LCN DNA findings approximately 21,000 times, although not all led to a prosecution.

The Home Office Forensic Regulator was to review how LCN findings were used and what should happen with the technique in the future. Although some scientists are unhappy with the method, many say that as long as the technique is applied correctly, all appropriate precautions are taken and the individual circumstances of cases are considered, then the findings are reliable.

The method may not produce an exact match with a person's DNA, which is why careful interpretation of the results using appropriate databases and software is so crucial. The technique is only used in two other countries for evidential purposes in criminal cases: the Netherlands and New Zealand.

Julie Ward

Julie Ward was a British photographer, whose burned and dismembered body was discovered in 1988, in the Masai Mara

Game Reserve, in Kenya. The official story was that she had been mauled to death by lions and her body was then struck by lightning.

Her father refused to accept this version of events and pursued an independent investigation. This investigation uncovered, among other things, that the coroner's report had been altered to cover the fact that Julie's bones had been cut with a sharp instrument rather than gnawed by animal teeth.

In 2008, Mr Ward was hopeful that DNA evidence would be of assistance in bringing to justice those who were responsible for his daughter's murder. It's now two years on and the Metropolitan police are still working with Kenyan authorities in an effort to solve the case.

All of the examples I've outlined above demonstrate why it is crucial not to accept everything presented in evidence at face value — challenge the assumptions at every turn. If there's a failing in the system, let's look at it, fix it, improve and move on.

Before we talk about what makes an expert an expert, let's linger briefly over one who is clearly anything but. Several cases of shonky forensic science spring to mind but, for me, the one that could make a Hollywood film is that of a truly bogus 'forensic scientist' from Manchester, England. This man had been passing himself off as a forensic investigator for 26 years. He worked on more than 700 cases, all of which will need to be assessed in case his testimony resulted in any miscarriages of justice. During that time, he fleeced the tax payer of at least £250,000 in payments. He is reported to have cut and pasted some of his reports from the Internet and even had a special fluorescent jacket made for him with FORENSIC INVESTIGATOR on the back.

He'd bought his qualifications (BSc in Forensic Science, a Masters with excellence in Forensic Investigation and a Doctorate in Criminology) from a sham university because, as he told the court, it 'looked easier' than going to a real university. To be fair, he's not wrong — training for anything is tough work but it doesn't mean we should all go around cheating, does it?

He was charged with many and varied things, including obtaining a money transfer by deception, obtaining property by deception, perverting the course of justice and perjury. The judge at his trial referred to him as an 'inveterate and compulsive liar'.

He was originally jailed for five years but I read recently that he was also charged and eventually convicted in December 2009 of sexual assault offences and is serving an indefinite term. Not really a poster boy for forensic scientists.

There's been an awful lot of brouhaha over the years about what makes an individual an expert in a given area. Many cases, unfortunately, can be used as examples to demonstrate what happens when forensic science goes bad. The lack of attention in the Damilola Taylor case is one, even though the scientists weren't deliberately trying to make a muck-up. The Birmingham Six case was a key factor in change within the police and one of the biggest shake-ups in British policing came with the introduction of the Police and Criminal Evidence Act 1984, now more commonly referred to as PACE. The job of PACE is to 'strike the right balance between the powers of the police and the rights and freedoms of the public' because they got in the doo-doo for beating confessions out of people, among other things. PACE is now constantly being updated (details are available on the Internet) because the government and the police recognise that modern policing changes as the population and the population-related problems change.

Forensic science in England and Wales had changed for the better as well and all was looking pretty good, but despite a tightening of controls and procedures within the forensic science agencies, more trouble was to come. The *CSI* effect led to literally hundreds of courses with the word 'forensic' in the title. A 2004 Home Office Science and Technology Select Committee identified that there was a 'poor standard of higher education forensic science provision'; the Forensic Science Occupational Committee of Skills for Justice stated that 'forensic science learning provision ... was not sufficiently preparing learners for employment in forensic science'.

New Zealand has the right idea I think — you can't study forensic science here at undergraduate level; you have to have at least a first degree in something scientific. Excellent idea. Otherwise, you end up with graduates with degrees that aren't useful for anything. At least with a full science degree a graduate has other options if forensic science doesn't work out. Plus they are given a full grounding in a decent science.

The good old US of A has had massive problems with the standards of its forensic science and they've also been undertaking a review. Some particularly awful cases have stoked the fires of reform in a substantial way, such as the case of Cameron Todd Willingham, who was convicted of killing his children in a house fire he allegedly set. Mr Willingham was executed in February 2004, still maintaining his innocence. A review of the case has since found that the forensic science used to convict him was inadequate. More action will probably occur on this matter, which seems to be only the tip of the iceberg of much needed reform.

In 2009, the USA National Research Council Committee on Identifying the Needs of the Forensic Sciences Community published a report entitled, *Strengthening Forensic Science in the United States: A Path Forward.*

The report says:

> *Because accused parties in criminal cases are convicted on the basis of testimony from forensic science experts, much depends upon whether the evidence offered is reliable. Furthermore, in addition to protecting innocent persons from being convicted of crimes that they did not commit, we are also seeking to protect society from persons who have committed criminal acts. Law enforcement officials and the members of society they serve need to be assured that forensic techniques are reliable. Therefore, we must limit the risk of having the reliability of certain forensic science methodologies judicially certified before the techniques have been properly studied and their accuracy verified by the forensic science community.*

Basically, this is the States saying that they don't want any more shonky forensic science, thanks very much, and we're going to do something about it, so shape up.

Overall, the report basically stated that the accuracy and reliability of practically all forensic science methods, ranging from glass to fingerprints, had not been established adequately through rigorous scientific scrutiny. The American Academy of Forensic Sciences (AAFS) annual conference in 2010 was tellingly entitled, *Putting Our Forensic House in Order: Determining Validation and Expelling Incompetence.*

So, not only is forensic science in the States being shaken upside down until the grotty bits drop out of its pockets, someone somewhere is getting paid to do the work that should have been done long ago, on an ongoing basis. Let's hope one of the resolutions that arises from the AAFS meeting is that forensic science techniques should be reviewed thoroughly now and regularly as time progresses. The situation is that if fundamental problems are found with a particular technique or evidence type, then convictions might be called into question, which could throw the whole system into disorder, incurring enormous expense and all the obvious associated problems.

To my mind, that's not a good enough reason not to do it. If people are sent to prison based, even in part, on scientific findings, then the science must be robust and reliable. If science is reviewed regularly and the law takes that into account then it should be possible to work out a system whereby the courts can be sure that the science is up-to-date, which in turn adds to the strength of science in court. It also might prevent the current stink that's going on in Texas over the inadequate forensic science presented in Cameron Todd Willingham's case.

In order to address the issues about forensic science in the States, academics at UCLA are being granted funds to consider error rates in latent fingerprint evidence. As I mentioned earlier, some would ask whether or not this sort of exercise should have been completed long ago. As with any other area of applied science, regular review should be undertaken. Unfortunately, this is not something that necessarily occurs in forensic science, partly because some agencies aren't keen on their databases being examined. I never had any problem reviewing glass or footwear mark databases when I was in England but who has ever fully analysed the data in national DNA databases?

Courtesy of the news media and programmes like *CSI*, we all know that DNA can be an extremely powerful tool in crime solution. When a sample from a crime scene is compared with a sample from an individual it should be the easiest thing to be able to say whether or not they originated from one and the same person, shouldn't it? In forensic science (and many other areas of science), without a solid and reliable database, interpretation of results can be troublesome or even meaningless. Once results have been obtained, a decision has to be made about how to report the findings so that the maximum amount of information can be gained from them. The way that's done varies between evidence types.

In cases involving physical fits, it can often be a simple case of yes, the pieces fitted together or no they didn't — conclusive either way, no grey areas. For other areas of forensic science it's a bit more complicated. DNA, for example, has a complex interpretation method based on statistical interpretation, which is part of the reason why DNA reporting in Victoria, Australia, was suspended at the latter end of 2009, temporarily halting the use of DNA in criminal cases because of a problem with interpretation of results after new technology was brought online in September. As a result of the new technology, more detailed information was obtained from DNA samples but the statistical models used to interpret the data were inadequate. In simple terms, it meant the DNA profiles could result in the wrong people being arrested, tried and convicted — miscarriage of justice, everyone's worst nightmare.

So who has checked all the databases that have been built up by police and prosecution agencies over the years? Who checks them to make sure the data is correctly entered or that the statistical basis for the interpretation is still correct and appropriate? As it turns out, the answer seems to be no one. An article in *New Scientist* entitled 'Unreliable evidence? Time to open up DNA databases' addressed this very issue. Most of the world's DNA results (and I am talking about those relating to criminal casework) are interpreted using the results of relatively small studies undertaken during the early years of DNA forensic casework. The opening two paragraphs of the article cover it quite nicely, I think:

> *When a defendant's DNA appears to match DNA found at a crime scene, the probability that this is an unfortunate coincidence can be central to whether the suspect is found guilty. The assumptions used to calculate the likelihood of such a fluke ... are now being questioned by a group of 41 scientists and lawyers based in the US and the United Kingdom. These assumptions have never been independently verified on a large sample of DNA profiles, says the group.*

I find that slightly unnerving, because I know from professional experience that if a DNA result is presented in court, it's unbelievably difficult to shake anyone's faith in the result. If the result is correct then there's no problem; we just need to make sure that it *is* correct.

Ignoring any other kind of DNA database for the moment, there are essentially two types of forensic DNA databases. The first is the crime scene database, which is the one that contains DNA profiles obtained from crime scene samples (so we don't know who is the source of the DNA). The second is the reference sample DNA database, which contains the results of samples taken from known people, usually suspects (depending on the legal jurisdiction). I'm not suggesting there is anything significantly wrong with any of the DNA databases but they should be open to examination by independent scientists, so the reliance placed on DNA interpretations can be shown to be well-placed. It makes the results relevant and reliable, which is important for acceptance as evidence in court. Plus we don't want situations where the wrong person goes to prison because of an incorrect match. The converse is that if a mistake was made entering a reference profile into a database, a comparison of a crime scene sample result with the reference samples might not show a match — we'd miss what could otherwise have been a 'hit'.

The big question is whether the FBI will allow a group of independent scientists to review the USA's CODIS database — and the answer at the moment is no. I can understand their reluctance in a way but I think it would be a better thing to have it reviewed now rather than wait for a specific case to demonstrate a monumental stuff-up and be beaten with the consequences later. It would also be better to have the data reviewed by people who would sign confidentiality agreements and then look at the data as a whole set rather than focusing on one case where there may well be a problem. Any doubts about the reliability of DNA databases could be scotched by allowing a review. We all have our dreams, and I hope the scientists' comes true.

I don't know whether the USA was inspired by the British to undertake their nationwide review of forensic sciences, but it's interesting that in 2008 the British government appointed a chap called the Forensic Science Regulator to start a review of forensic science. One of the major things he did was shut down the Council for the Registration of Forensic Practitioners (CRFP), which was a bit of a shock. Not least because I paid a load of renewal subscription money for being reassessed in several areas and it took me over a year to get any of it back. As I understand it, it wasn't that the CRFP was doing anything wrong, more that it wasn't doing it very efficiently. It was originally set up to bring some kind of regulation and accreditation to the forensic science industry and partly to keep out people like the now-jailed Mancunian imposter. It had been funded by the government and had the backing of MPs and all kinds of important people, but it just couldn't quite get to where it needed to be. Still, these things have to start somewhere.

As one of the few professional bodies in England and Wales dealing specifically with the forensic sciences, the Forensic Science Society had many things to say on the subject of the review. Among their comments was this: 'Experience is not necessarily expertise although expertise is based on experience.' The Society has a very good point.

The Forensic Regulator is currently producing a Forensic Science Standards Guidance Manual that will detail how he plans to identify, develop, implement and enforce quality standards relating to the provision of forensic science services to the Criminal Justice System.

Once he's decided what makes an expert an expert, I'll let you know. In the meantime, I generally fall back on the old favourites that include making sure people doing the forensic science are trained and qualified, other people recognise them to be so, they use methods that are tried, tested, reliable and don't have a bad reputation — all pretty standard stuff, you'd think. And, as the Forensic Science Society rightly suggests, parties should check whether there is 'any evidence to suggest the expert may not be impartial' — this applies to both sides.

As a result of the issues I've outlined above, casework in England and Wales is now, and has been for many years, routinely examined by solicitors and barristers, whether the matters be criminal, civil, insurance, Family, Youth or whatever other tribunal. If a lawyer receives a specialist report of any kind they pick up the phone and talk to a relevant specialist to get some advice. Forensic scientists are very used to independent experts coming in to view their work and examine exhibits; they know it's just a quality control check to make sure everything is fully, fairly and accurately reported. In many cases, they know that the *real* work for the independent expert is in reinterpreting the information based on a new set of circumstances described by the defendant. Not that we tell them that's what we're doing or what those new circumstances are! Most prosecution experts have been to court enough times to know that the scientific issues at court aren't usually about what they've reported but about what the defence says they mean based on the defendant's account of events. Everything is very open and friendly between the scientists because we all know that complete access to the information makes life easier for all concerned. The Criminal Procedure and Civil Procedure Rules facilitate this approach and it means the working day is much easier and giving evidence in court is much less stressful.

New Zealand on the other hand has a totally different approach to the matter. It is relatively unusual for independent experts to attend the laboratories of ESR Forensic. Compare that with independent scientists in England and Wales who visit 'prosecution' laboratories a couple of times a week (depending on their areas of expertise). Population size is not really the defining factor because I estimate that in England and Wales each independent company (each containing a variety of specialists) serves a couple of million people and undertakes several hundred reports each year. Compare that with New Zealand where the amount of cases subjected to thorough scientific review is a small fraction of that undertaken in the United Kingdom. This confirms the view expressed to me by some criminal law barristers that New Zealand cases tend to be challenged on technical legal grounds. To me, the most sensible way forward is to at least consider the whole shebang, which also then fulfils the lawyer's duties as set out in the Lawyers and Conveyancers Act (Lawyers: Conduct and Client Care) Rules 2008. These rules are made in accordance with the Lawyers and Conveyancers Act 2006, the purposes of this Act being, among other things, 'to maintain public confidence in the provision of legal services'. As a forensic scientist, I want to make sure that if science is used to put someone in prison, it's the right person and for the right scientific reasons.

I don't know what the US and UK reviews will finally say but the thing to remember is that if the overall outcomes and the work being carried out to address those outcomes identifies some real problems, the implications could be felt throughout court systems worldwide — including New Zealand. We shall just have to watch and see.

Chapter 6

The arena

Court buildings are as varied in appearance, atmosphere and setting as the cases heard within their walls. Some modern courts are just plain hideous and when I say 'modern' I mean post-war or 1970s and it seems to be the lower courts that suffer the most — Magistrates' Courts or District Courts.

Guildford Magistrates' Court in Surrey, England, is a vile box of a monstrosity: rain-streaked grey concrete overlying dull brown brick, wedged between two main roads and a municipal car park. It's hard to describe it in any unique or distinguishing way because nothing about it is either unique or distinguishing; it just looks like so many other grey, concrete, two-level office blocks. Given that it's so vile, you'd think urban planners would have learnt and wouldn't make the same mistake again. Oh, how wrong it is possible to be. Just down the road in Aldershot (which, interestingly, is easily mis-typed as Aldershit) is a repeat offender, this time in a slightly paler shade of grey. The car park surrounds it and the ring road is right outside the front door. The oppressiveness continues inside, in charmless rooms, orange plastic chairs in the waiting area, brown/cream cracked melamine-topped counters and a school toilet. The court seats are slightly better — of the fabric-covered variety but sit on an industrial strength brown carpet and windowless corridors.

On the other hand, some lower courts are lovely, such as Chelmsford Magistrates. A beautiful open entry hall with high ceilings, tiled flooring and carved wooden handrails. Some courts are just surprising. North Somerset District Court is lovely and airy but has a strange pile of stones out the front — perhaps they had some money left over and didn't know what to spend it on. The parking is excellent, though, and free.

Manukau District Court is quite pleasing on the eye from the outside and it hasn't aged too badly considering how many cases they hear and the number of people thronging through the front doors on a Monday morning, which is a busy court day because it's the first chance to hear cases involving people who got locked up over the weekend. The first time I was at Manukau was as a mere forensic science assistant, not long after it first opened. The carpets were new and the interior walls freshly painted. The exterior glass walls on the ground floor were sparkly in the sunshine and it only felt a *tiny* little bit like being in a goldfish bowl. I looked around as two families exited the building through the shiny, sliding glass front doors and decided that if I had to be giving evidence in court, this was as nice a place as any to do it. As I glanced out through the clean, shiny windows, admiring the freshness of the whole place, my eyes happened upon two large men advancing swiftly on one another in the car park, each part of the family groups I had just seen leaving the brand new reception area. The splendid new windows blocked out the sound so it was like watching TV on mute. Three seconds later there was a full-on (silent) fist fight, complete with (silently) screaming women, grappling police officers trying to prise the two apart followed by (silently mouthed) arrests. My overall impressions were that perhaps the sliding front doors might be better replaced with revolving ones and that life in a court building is a roller coaster of unexpected events. Perhaps there is some irony in being able stand in the car park and watch people on a *real* roller coaster at Rainbow's End amusement park.

Auckland District Court is another kettle of fish entirely. It's drab and oppressive and there is no parking anywhere nearby that doesn't cost an arm, a leg or a towtruck. Other courts are the usual sort of mundane, functional government department-type building that doesn't really register a memory or a specific mention. Overall, though, I have to say that New Zealand courts tend to smell less malodorous than English ones.

The higher courts, such as Crown and High Courts, are often stunning. I divide them into two sorts. The traditional, prominent, imposing edifice that radiates formality that has a kind of pressurised force field around it that increases as you reach the doors, although that could be psychological. The second sort seems to have been built to break that traditional mould of oppression. They tend to be light and airy with big windows and carpeted floors. I personally really like Auckland High Court because it has a bit of both sorts, with a huge stained glass entranceway; it neatly blends new architecture with the original building.

As you go through the second set of entrance doors, there's a little corridor that slides off into part of the old court — it's like discovering a secret passageway. There's also a little café in the main foyer with very frank notices on the walls basically saying that loose lips sink ships: don't talk about your case in a loud voice because you might give the game away to someone on the other side. It's the only court I've ever visited where they point out the very thing that everyone does (even unintentionally) but to which no one likes to admit.

Christchurch High Court, on the other hand, is a large grey-brown monster with no character whatsoever, and lifts that take forever to arrive. On days when I feel energetic I race up the stairs to see if I can get to the fifth floor before the lift. The view from the top is fantastic, though — right across to the Southern Alps. When the experts from the United Kingdom were over for the Bain retrial, a glimpse through the snow clouds to the mountains was all they saw of New Zealand's southern magnificence.

One would think that the Crown Court in Cambridge, England, would be a fantastic seat of judicial finery, being as it's located in one of the most famous educational cities in the world. Cambridge was inhabited as far back as the Bronze Age and the modern city was formally founded in 875 AD by invading Danes. Having a population of around 2000 by the time the Domesday Book was written in 1086, Cambridge went from strength to strength. In the early 1200s, hostile townsmen scared some scholars away from Oxford, who took refuge in Cambridge. From that was born the start of the university.

Given that illustrious history, what possessed an architect and the local council to design and construct a court building on the ring road that looks like a multi-storey car park? In its infinite wisdom, the local council has also taken away most of the directional road signs from the Cambridge ring road. This is supposed to discourage people from driving into and around the city, thus encouraging them to use the Park & Ride bus transport system. What it actually does is cause more traffic, because so many people don't know about the lack of road signs until it's too late and they end up driving round and round and *round* until they end up trying to drive into the Crown Court because it looks like a car park and they're desperate to park their car. Failing to find an entrance to the apparent car park, they turn round and head out of the city, presumably to somewhere with less traffic phobia, like Scotland.

There are, of course, other famous seats of judicial loveliness, such as the Central Criminal Court, which is located in the street for which it is also informally named, Old Bailey. The Old Bailey is located just outside the official City of London, near Newgate Prison. This was a convenient location for transport of prisoners to the court for their trials and a convenient return trip to the prison and the gallows if they were found guilty. The last public hanging at Newgate, which involved use of the portable gallows, took place in 1868 and in 1907 it was the site of the last private hanging. The court itself was extensively remodelled just after this.

The first time I attended the Central Criminal Court was with a colleague; he had written a fire report, I had written a footwear report. We travelled down together and were met at the front door of the court building by the junior barrister. It's an imposing place, the Central Criminal Court, not just because of its notoriety but also because of its incredible security-rich entrance area. The main entrance is an understated affair that's easy to walk past if you don't know where to go. Once inside the revolving door, you're in a corridor formed by the exterior wall on the right and a long glass window on the left. Official security-type people watch you through that window. You advance towards what look like two airlocks. Only one person at any one time passes through each airlock. You can't enter the airlock until the person in front has cleared the other side. The front door of the airlock is activated by a pressure pad on the floor. You then step into the airlock and the door closes behind you, so it's not for the claustrophobic, even though it's all transparent. The glass panel in front of you then opens and you can step out, followed by the door closing behind you. And then the security really begins — the usual emptying of pockets into a tray, an airport security-like walkthrough, hand-held body scanners, X-ray for bags and pocket contents, visual and physical pat-down then a tick-off on the list of expected visitors before you are released into the waiting area to wait for your chaperone to arrive and accompany you to the relevant part of the court.

After we'd negotiated the Star Trek arrivals hall, we were taken up a set of wide stone staircases to the first floor. On the way up the stairs, our attention was directed to a seemingly innocuous object protruding from high on a brush-painted and otherwise featureless wall. In the 1970s the 'Troubles' between the British and the Irish in Northern Ireland took a new turn. Before then, the IRA hadn't targeted mainland England. In March 1973, a car bomb went off outside the Central Criminal Court, killing one man and injuring more than one hundred others. The blast blew window glass and debris into the Central Criminal Court and the innocuous-looking object in the wall was a fragment of that glass, left there when the frontage was rebuilt, 'lest we forget'. It's a very real reminder of the fear that gripped England, and me as a child, for a long time. As a lawyer in England during the 1970s and 1980s, my mum remembers court windows being fitted with special long, net-style curtains. They hung down like normal curtains but finished off in what looked like a window box running along the windowsill level. There was plenty of spare material in the length of the curtain so that if a bomb went off outside and the window glass was shattered and blown into the court, the reinforced net-type curtains would billow inwards with the force of the explosion and catch the glass fragments, thus sparing the people in the building from being sprayed with flying, and possibly fatal, shards.

The embedded glass fragment at the Old Bailey is why they make you go through such a robust security check when entering the court. Not just to prevent terrorists taking bombs into the court but also to protect court users from those unbalanced members of society who have otherwise not been restrained or treated successfully — I believe it's called Care in the Community. Security procedures are also to keep people inside the court buildings safe from convicted criminals, those about to be convicted, disgruntled partners/spouses/children, violent friends and/or family of defendants, bearing in mind that the worst criminal cases are heard at the Old Bailey.

Once you've negotiated the security, if you're lucky you get to go to the old part of the Central Criminal Court, with its carved wooden doorways, hand-painted murals on ceilings and walls, heavy wooden courtroom doors and incredibly crowded courtrooms. The courtroom I visited on that occasion wasn't crowded in that there were too many people because, quite frankly, you can't fit too many people in because of the enormous mass of timber. The dock was right in the middle of the courtroom and raised up high and it was a huge dock, too. Counsel was relegated to a very low place below the bench (which is where the judge sits), the witness box and the jury seats. It was confusing as a witness because you are taught to address the jury as the trier of fact, which is pretty difficult when the witness box is at one end of the jury seats — I was within spitting distance of the first two jurors but couldn't see the other end of the jury at all, which meant that they couldn't see me. Apart from the occasion when I was heavily pregnant and the jurors at the very end of the rows could see my fidgety belly sticking out. It was very bizarre.

All other English, Scottish and Welsh courts have, to my knowledge, less stringent but generally effective security features when compared with the Old Bailey. They have permanent, fixed-to-the-floor walk-through metal detectors like the ones they have at the airport, unlike New Zealand where they wheel them into position occasionally, seemingly dependent on whether there are funds to pay for security staff. I thought that might change when a man in Wellington managed to take a knife into court and stab himself in the neck when he was being sentenced. The metal detectors were at court but weren't being used that day.

Many people underestimate the importance of preparation. Time spent in preparation is never wasted; and it's vitally important to prepare for going to court. Giving evidence is the pinnacle of what it means to be an expert witness and forensic scientist. The original meaning of forensic related to the marketplace, or debate in a public forum, and now relates largely to a court of law. Forensic does not mean scientific evidence.

I've established my own rules for getting ready for court, none of which I have ever seen taught in the formal setting of a classroom or lecture theatre. They're not hard and fast, and like all rules, are sometimes broken. Just like learning to drive a car, one learns how to drive by the rule book then one uses one's accumulating experience to decide which ones can be bent (rules that is, not vehicles).

Rule 1

One working day before you're due to go to court, check with your instructing party to confirm you are definitely still required to attend at the time and date previously agreed. Contacting your instructing party more than one day in advance gives circumstances a chance to change drastically. There's a good chance that the state of play at 4.30 p.m. the evening beforehand will match the circumstances at 9 a.m. on the day you're due to give evidence.

Rule 2

Having established that you will definitely be required to attend court, decide what you're going to wear. Make sure it's clean and ironed. Take your clothes to a room where, tomorrow morning, you will be able to get dressed with the light on despite sunrise not being due for three hours after you've left the house. This is unless you live on your own, in which case you can wander around in the buff to your heart's content, looking for that lost sock.

I learnt about getting dressed with the light on from the man who went to court wearing one tan shoe and one black shoe — all because he'd got dressed in the dark. The impression he set was less 'sophisticated, highly trained and experienced expert witness' and more 'wandered out from local institute because they left the front door unlocked at breakfast time', particularly as he didn't notice until it was too late to nip to a local shoe shop.

Rule 3

Always carry a small amount of cash for emergency situations. All courts are different, all parking situations at said courts are different. Even travelling by public transport has its risks of cash outlay including unexpected delays requiring purchase of drinks and sustenance. Some public toilets, such as those at King's Cross in London (even Platform 9¾) require money to gain access to said facilities, although presumably Hogwarts pupils can just magic their way in. Public car parks are unpredictable in location and cost — Brownies, Guides, Cubs and Scouts: Be Prepared.

Rule 4

Always, always arrive early at court so you can scope out the landscape, find the courtroom and check for the tenth time that you've got a working pen and some paper.

Rule 5

Take tissues (possibly more relevant for women). Not for unexpected emotion, but for lack of toilet rolls. One particular court springs to mind — it has blue lighting to stop drug users seeing their veins for shooting up. It also has no locks on the doors, no toilet seats, metal sheeting instead of mirrors (desperate people can slash their wrists with broken mirror glass; it's pretty hard to break sheet metal) and no toilet rolls. The toilets in question have never pretended to have toilet rolls — there aren't any toilet roll dispensers. These toilets have never pretended to have toilet seats either — not sure why; the only thing I could think of was not being able to use them as weapons. Of all the courts I've been in, this one could have learnt from the way things were done in London's Central Criminal Court in the early 1900s, when there were separate waiting rooms for ladies and gentlemen with yet another separate room for 'the better class'.

Rule 6
Turn off your mobile phone once you've met up with your instructing counsel — they're the only people who count until you've given evidence and are no longer required at court for that particular case that day.

Rule 7
Always make sure you have your name ticked off on an official clipboard as soon as you arrive at court. If the officials who run the court don't know you were there and the time you arrived, even if you give evidence in a case, you run the risk of not getting paid.

Rule 8 (courtesy of a former colleague)
When you've been released from a case, run like the clappers until you're out of sight of the front door and don't turn on your phone again until you're at least an hour away.

Chapter 7

The lion's mouth

Lawyers rarely do more than minimally review the qualifications of the expert and verify the facts on which the expert conclusions are based. The voir dire examination is typically based upon perfunctory questioning about institutional affiliation and publications. The reason for this limited inquiry is simple: most lawyers and judges lack the adequate scientific background to argue or decide the admissibility of expert testimony.

Neufeld & Coleman, 1990

Douglas Adams once wrote about a rain god in his book *So Long, and Thanks for All the Fish.* This guy was a long distance lorry driver who happened to be a rain god. He didn't know he was a rain god but the clouds loved him and followed him around everywhere. He saw so much rain that he classified it. I'm not a rain god but I think I've been stuck behind him on many a long, court-related journey. I like to try to classify the rain when I'm travelling, whether I'm stuck in a traffic jam on the Auckland Harbour Bridge or peering out at the drizzle blowing horizontally across the runway at

Christchurch airport, just so it doesn't depress me any more than it already has. The only time when I haven't been that bothered about the rain was when I was landing at an airport in one of those planes that are so narrow you can stretch out your arms and touch opposite sides of the cabin at the same time. From your seat. On that occasion, the plane was coming in at such an angle that when I looked out of the cockpit window (because there are no doors to the cockpit either), I couldn't see the runway. That was because I could see it out to my left — the cross-wind was *very* strong (no, it wasn't Wellington) and we were coming in at a strong angle to compensate; the rain really didn't seem that important at that point.

I've travelled a lot in my time and I've seen a lot of rain. There are lots of different types of rain. Sumatran rain is hard and merciless, but precise in where it stops and starts — you can literally draw a line on the ground where it has decided not to rain. Auckland rain is similar but with more wind. Scottish rain is bitingly cold and, in the highlands, often horizontal. Canary Islands rain is warm and not cleansing at all. It somehow manages to make you feel more grimy than before it rained, but that could just be the gentle wafting of rehydrated vomit and stale beer recently deposited by Brits abroad on a stag week. Australian rain sometimes doesn't even touch the ground because it's so hot. However, of all the rain I've ever encountered English rain depresses me the most. It's grey, dreary and incessant. I once heard a description of an English winter as like being stuck inside a Tupperware box for six months of the year.

I have never been more concerned about the type of rain

than the time I went to court in a drugs case. The memory of this case came rushing back to me when I gave a talk to the Auckland Executive Club. I put up a photo of some fragments of cannabis resin, to provide an example of the sort of casework I've done. As I looked at it, the memories barged through some door at the back of my brain, careered into my thinking area and clogged up the view.

The case itself wasn't difficult: the defendant was claiming that the weight of cannabis resin reported by the police was incorrect — he said it was less than reported. He also said he had cut up some of the resin using a knife with a serrated edge. I had to go to the forensic science laboratory, examine the resin, weigh it, confirm it was correctly reported and check the cut faces for signs of having been cut with a serrated knife of the type that was supplied to me. The resin had started off as a whole block and was described as such by the Crown scientist, although she commented that it was quite dry and friable. However, after it had been driven 300 kilometres back to the police station and then back to the lab for my examination, it had broken into pieces. Small, small pieces. Not a problem — all part of the job. I spent a happy few hours trying to piece the bits together to confirm that the cannabis was, indeed, the same as that described by the arresting officer and the Crown scientist. Once I established that, in fact, no one had pinched any or added any to it, and that it was so fragmented I couldn't tell what was a cut edge and what was a sheared face, I went on my merry way, back to the office to write the report and post it to the solicitors.

So, what was the bad memory that swept over me when I was giving my presentation to the Executive Club? The court appearance, that's what. Travelling to and from court can be quite nice — a bit of a jolly, out from the office for extremely legitimate reasons, sometimes a nice, short day if the Hearing is within an hour's drive of home and is heard in the morning. Always unpredictable, though. As usual, I had checked with the instructing party the day before and he confirmed that, yes, I would be required.

To make it to court by 9.30 a.m. I had to leave home at five. Crappy weather, raining and cold. Decisions, decisions: go along the back roads or take the motorway. I opted for the latter but got stuck in a two-hour traffic jam. There was a small glimmer of pleasure when I heard on the radio that there was a 10 kilometre tailback on my alternative route so it wouldn't have mattered which way I went. By this time, the radio breakfast show had finished, which meant two things: It was 9 a.m. and I wasn't even halfway there yet and there was no decent radio programme for at least another hour. There was a car fire on the motorway ahead — delay for 45 minutes. By now, it was 9.15 a.m. so I telephoned the solicitor to advise I was running late. I wouldn't get a ticket from the cops because the car was stationary, had been for some time, the handbrake was on, and they were all at the car fire up ahead anyway. I advised the solicitor I'd be there in time for a 10 a.m. start in court. However, I had woefully underestimated the time taken to negotiate a car fire. Eventually, I arrived in the right general location at 11 a.m. but couldn't find the court. When I eventually did find it, tucked behind some trees with no road signage, there was nowhere to park, despite the solicitor advising me yesterday that there was loads of parking and, no, I wouldn't need any change for a parking meter.

I rolled into court with cramp in my legs having spent six and a half hours driving across the country in the pouring rain and what did the barrister say when I got there? 'Who are you?'

Rather than poking him in the eye and storming off, which is what I wanted to do, I explained to him that my presence was requested, by his solicitor. 'Oh, your report was agreed by the prosecution yesterday. You really should have rung to check that you were required; my client changed his plea to guilty last night. I'm not sure whether your fees can be paid, seeing as we didn't know you were coming.' Strangely enough, the instructing solicitor, whom I had rung while I was on my way to court, wasn't actually at court, even though he told me he was.

So, what did I do? What could I do? I got back in my car, turned round and took five hours to get home, swearing most of the way, still trying to find something decent to listen to on the radio. Inevitably, I became stuck in the rubber-neckers traffic going past the car fire in the opposite direction because let's face it, it was a big fire and I'd only gone past it 40 minutes previously. Total of my day: 10 and a half hours driving in drizzly winter weather, five minutes at court (including three using the bathroom), no court appearance, more time spent 'at work' than on a normal day. To this day, I wonder if the solicitor was ever actually at court and if he was, whether he hid when I arrived because he should have told me not to come. Or whether he got me mixed up with another case he was doing that day. I classified the rain that day as grey, depressing drizzle, persistent and likely to last for some time.

Having made it to court and actually being required to do something when you get there, there is the potential problem of having to get up and speak in front of a lot of people you don't know.

Many people have a fear of public speaking and I was no exception. I swore I would never *ever* give another presentation to my peers after a particularly harrowing experience presenting some research findings as a soft-bellied, freshly hatched PhD graduate. Quite how I ended up giving evidence once or twice a week for six years is quite beyond me — it just sort of happened. Giving evidence in New Zealand happens less often, but, as with buses, court appearances seem to come irregularly and generally in groups of three. Giving evidence to a court is the part of being an expert witness that, to be honest, no one really thinks about when they get into the job. Even when people are asked about it in a job interview, you can see them lie through their eye teeth about how they're absolutely fine with the idea, the key word here being 'idea'. By the time they realise how tough it is, it's too late. The prospect of even contemplating giving evidence reduces the strongest constitution to a sweaty, clammy amoeba with damp hands and armpits and a pasty pallor. And that's before they've even actually got to court. It's just one of those things you can either handle or you can't. If you can't, it's going to be a short career.

I'm not even sure if you ever get used to doing it. Each court appearance is different, each case is different, all the personalities involved are different — if anything the only thing I can say about it is, in the words of Forrest Gump, you never know what you're gonna get. It's definitely not as nice as a box of chocolates. It's often said that if you don't get nervous before going to court then you've done something wrong.

The blood starts to pump when you open the file at the office and read through it — that's when it goes one way or the other. Either you read through it and know instantly that you worded the key sections of text appropriately so that you can be stronger in what you have to say when you're in the witness box, if necessary. Or you find a blinding error and your whole blood supply flashes round your body in less than a second on its way to the surface of your skin to bring you out in the most almighty panic sweat in the history of creation.

Thankfully, the latter has only happened once. It was a case I'd prepared when I was heavily pregnant and the court date had been set especially for me, based on my return-to-work date three months later. It was a drink-drive case in Wales, so it was going to entail a very early start in the morning. I can see it clear as day in my head: I was at home, it was warm and light outside so it must have been late summer. I read the report after dinner and there it was — the last line of the last paragraph of the conclusions. I'd missed out a word. Instead of reading *Mr X's indicated pattern of alcohol consumption could not have given rise to the recorded breath alcohol reading*, it said *Mr X's indicated pattern of alcohol consumption could have given rise to the recorded breath alcohol reading*. I'd missed out the word 'not'. It didn't matter that it was correct in an earlier part of the report, the fact was that none of the solicitors ever read the main body of the report in drink-drive cases — they always skipped to the Summary/Conclusions section.

It also didn't matter that my boss had missed it when he'd peer-reviewed it — although it might be true and it might be his responsibility to make sure my report was correct (you never see your own mistakes, or not at least until it's too late). Such excuses count for diddly squat in the witness box. In fact, such excuses would not even be made. The simple response in the witness box is *I apologise. That was my error* and move right along.

It was the absence of that one teeny tiny word that was the reason for my having to attend court. The gist of the paragraph was that the defendant's story about what he had drunk before and after the incident was credible — it went directly to the heart of the issue, the ultimate issue: whether or not the defendant was guilty. Credibility is hugely important in drink-driving cases because often there's only one account of what the defendant drank, and that's the defendant's account. Here I was saying that the defendant's account was credible when what I actually meant in science speak was that *he was wrong about what he'd drunk*. The total opposite of what I'd written. Panic, panic, sweat, sweat, deep breaths.

Fortunately, I had the solicitor's mobile phone number written on the file (which I now always do, in case of emergencies). I rang him and had to admit my appalling mistake. He was very gracious and I didn't bore him with any efforts to appease the mistake or explain why it had happened. Like I say, no one cares how the mistake happens, they just want someone to hang for it.

I can guarantee the solicitor will have gone into court the following day and made an absolute meal of the whole episode, largely so his client wouldn't have to pay costs for wasting court time. That will have been squarely set at my door. For once I was being blamed for something in court and it really was my fault. I tell you what, it's never happened again. The next time I had a baby, I doubled my maternity leave and took six months, just to ensure my 'baby brain' had subsided.

The other response to having to attend court is to just refuse. However, if you *do* refuse, there will be a lot of very angry people. I've actually been there when it's happened. I prepared a report for the defence in an alleged rape case. It was a very straightforward report about the drugs that were detected in the blood sample of the woman who had made the complaint to the police, and what they meant in terms of how she would have been affected by them at the time of the alleged incident. From memory, she was more drunk than anything else. Anyway, the expert for the prosecution suddenly decided when we were at court and after the trial had been going for three days that she couldn't bring herself to give evidence. Mad panic in the prosecution camp — they had to draft in another expert. If a defence witness had decided they didn't want to give evidence because they were out of their depth, they'd probably lose their job.

I ask you now to clear your mind and accompany me on a journey, a journey along a winding, rocky road of discovery. A road that leads to enlightenment, release and the ultimate destination of one's inner being. No, you don't need to check the cover of the book — you're still reading the same thing. I just want to get you in the mood for imagining. Perhaps I should stick to my day job.

Anyway, imagine if you will, the arrival of a letter through the post at work saying, *The Crown in the case of R v Bloggs has indicated it does not accept the report of Dr Sandiford. He* [yet one example of many assumptions by someone who hasn't read my statement and seen that my name is Anna, not Andrew] *will therefore be required to attend court to give evidence at 9.30 a.m. on 7 April.* It was the first letter of its type I'd ever seen (i.e. one with my name on it), it was to be the first time I would give evidence in court and it was a scary thing. I tried not to let it show.

Where was I going to have to go to give evidence? Maybe Bristol. That way I could stay with family the night before and not have to worry about being late or trying to find the court. No such luck. It was Crawley. Where the hell is Crawley? The only thing close to Crawley I knew was a fallen angel called Crowley in Terry Pratchett and Neil Gaiman's book *Good Omens*, who had invented the M25 London Orbital Motorway as a way of calling the Son of the Devil onto Earth during Armageddon. The suggestion that the M25 is a design of Beelzebub is not an unreasonable one in my opinion and probably the opinion of several million other people from around the world, having spent many, many, *many* hours stationary in the outside lane near Heathrow. Given the state of the English motorway system, I decided not to chance it and got the train instead.

At that time, the use of drug trace evidence in the courts was still being thrashed out and this case didn't look to be any different. For two weeks I trekked up and down to Crawley, to sit in court, advise the barrister, listen to possibly relevant testimony, make notes and generally get used to the court environment. More than once I met the barrister on the Tube and every time she insisted on calling me Alison, even though my name is Anna. Even the barrister for the Crown knew my name, but not my own instructing counsel. Was it arrogance, rudeness or just lack of seeing the wood for the trees? I don't know but it did start to irritate me after the first week.

In terms of actually giving evidence, luckily for me, the judge decided that he wanted the drug trace findings to be tested through a voir dire, which is essentially a trial within a trial. The jury was released for the day and the evidence was heard by the judge alone so that he could decide whether or not it was admissible. This for me was the ideal situation because it meant I got to have a dry run at it before having to give evidence in front of a real, live jury. The judge wasn't bothered about niceties; he just wanted to hear the gist of what each expert was going to say.

I was, at that time, seven months' pregnant and let me say that I did not carry pregnancy well. None of the lovely maternal glow for me. It was more of a lank, pale look of permanent tiredness. The prosecution expert on the other hand was style personified. Here we were then with me looking lank and peaky and the prosecution expert looking resplendent and perky.

I don't remember much about actually giving evidence in either the voir dire or the trial proper, only that I was glad when it was over. We were all standing outside the courtroom afterwards and the Crown barrister asked me when my baby was due, and do you know what? My own instructing barrister hadn't even noticed I was pregnant.

❄

Courts are usually fairly civilised in their treatment of expert witnesses. Sure, there are discrepancies when you're at court as a 'defence' expert. For example, you're not provided with the same comfort facilities as the Crown witnesses. In England and Wales, the inner sanctum is called the Witness Services private room where Crown witnesses get free tea and coffee, a paper to read and, more importantly, a heater and an indication of what's happening with the case. The Witness Services room also houses the police officers and they know what's going on because at least one of them is allowed in the courtroom, regardless of what's happening in there. Most witnesses aren't allowed in court until they actually give evidence, just so that they don't align their account of events with any previous witnesses.

Generally speaking, it's not too much of a problem being without the prosecution expert's additional comfort benefits, except where there is a high risk of being in close contact with a defendant or their family, friends or, in some cases, enemies. Even then, it's usually possible to avoid any physical or verbal contact if you wear your best 'I'm a lawyer and I'm not *your* lawyer' face.

On more than one occasion, security guards have had to separate opposing factions in a case. There was one memorable occasion where the main defence witness was a man who had previously been the defendant's best friend. Unfortunately, between the date of giving statements to the police and the date of the court appearance the defendant and his 'best mate' had a monumental falling out, which resulted in the witness/former best mate refusing to go to court to give evidence. The court had to issue a warrant for the former best mate's arrest, which made the defendant very agitated, especially when he saw the police car heading off down the road with its blues and twos (blue lights on top of the car and two-tone siren) going and three burly police officers squashed in the back. Forty minutes later the police car returned with three burly police officers plus a bedraggled-looking man who had been forcefully removed from both his shower and his house in order to give evidence for a man he described as a rather unpleasant chap (or four letter words to that effect). The case went downhill from there from the defendant's point of view, although it hadn't been looking too good beforehand. It was a bonus spectator sport for the people standing around the court foyer waiting for their cases to be called — it's not often you see a half-naked, soaking wet bloke being dragged through a court by police officers.

I was once required to attend court in a case involving drug traces on banknotes. I knew the other expert, we got on well, he realised the limitations of his evidence and, even better, he was prepared to acknowledge them on the stand — saved me a lot of time, effort and grief and there was no need for a distracting mud-slinging match about how much should or shouldn't be read into the scientific findings. He was there for the Crown and I was there for the defence. When we first walked in that morning, there was a large contingent of armed police manning the entry doors, the metal detectors, the courtroom doors and the toilets, which in itself was unusual. I saw the Crown's expert approaching and behind him a scuffle breaking out between heavily armed police and some of the supporters of whoever was being prosecuted. At this point, my Crown counterpart saw what was happening, legged it up the stairs two at a time and into the Witness Services room — I swear I could hear the door bang behind him, probably as he leaned his entire body weight against it from the other side. Maybe I didn't hear that — perhaps it was just the pounding of fear behind my eyeballs as more firearms appeared and the scuffling and yelling increased. I couldn't even run to the toilet — remember, armed police in the way. No one was shot, though, which was good.

There are exceptions to the no-niceties-for-the-defence-expert rule, of course. I was allowed to watch TV in the security guard's office at a court once because they knew the defendant, they knew there wasn't a chance he'd appear at the appointed time (or ever) and the heating was broken in the main waiting room. They were right — he never showed. Just as well really, because if I gave evidence (even though I was there at the instructions of his solicitor) it would have crucified him, he would not have been allowed to pass Go and he would not have been allowed to collect $200.

A very nice lady at one particular court used to make me a cup of tea when I went there, mostly because I always seemed to be pregnant but also because the tea from the vending machine looked like brown wee — probably tasted like it too. Why do they make the tea like that? Surely, it's not good for business, or do they know they've got a captive market? No one dares leave the building once they enter, just in case their case is called and a warrant for their arrest is issued in their absence. *Sorry your Worships, I was just getting a cuppa — the tea here looks like brown wee* probably won't wash as an excuse.

Having said the court experience is usually OK, I've seen

some pretty bad treatment of experts and some pretty bad behaviour on the part of court staff; these are exceptions (I hope) so there's no need to think these things happen all the time. It's just that when they do, they really stand out.

In one case, for example, the defendant was visibly upset during one part of the Crown's case where graphic photographs of the deceased were shown to the court. The jury asked for the defendant to be provided with a box of tissues. During one of the breaks when the defendant and the jury were out of the court, a member of the court staff slammed a box of tissues down on the table where the defendant would be seated and said in front of some members of the media, *'These are for Mr fucking Bloggs.'* Unprofessional at the very least, regardless of what he may have thought. I guess it's a function of working in courts all the time; law of averages says that court staff see some pretty bad stuff and bad people but keeping a professional lid on personal opinion is vital.

On another occasion I was one of three expert witnesses at court giving evidence for the defence. One of us was only part way through giving his evidence when the court was adjourned. When this happens, the person giving evidence mustn't discuss anything to do with the case with anyone. We all left the courtroom and asked our colleague if he would like a drink. As he walked towards us to tell us he'd like a tea with sugar, he was physically restrained by a police officer and shoved into a back office. It was overkill and insulting.

I've had my fair share of unwarranted scowling and hostility from police officers but most of them ask me the same question. How can you do the work that gets these scumbags/criminals/thieves/[insert expletives] off? The answer of course is that I don't. That's not my job and that's not what it's all about. It's not my job to have an opinion on whether a person is guilty or not guilty, so most of the time I don't think about it. I don't usually know the whole picture so I can't make an informed decision. Occasionally, I've had a case that has penetrated the thick wall I've developed over the years, but thankfully those are few and far between.

Whenever I give evidence I sit outside court so that I know what is happening and when I'll be required. Sometimes, I advise other witnesses (whether they're part of my case or not) on what to expect when giving evidence; for defence lay witnesses there's sometimes no one else there outside the courtroom, they've forgotten what the barrister told them and they have no idea what it's all about. Unfortunately, the *CSI* effect kicks in and they think it's going to be like it is on the telly.

On the basis of having attended court hundreds of times and having given evidence on many of those occasions, I have established my own set of rules.

1   Be 100 per cent happy with what you are going to be saying before you go into court. Confidence is key.

2   You will often be asked a question that requires a simple yes or no answer. You know the answer is not as simple. You know the person asking the question also knows that and they know you know that they know. So don't just answer yes or no. Shift the answer around so you put your proviso in first and finish off with either yes or no. This allows you to present the information the

court needs in order to be properly informed and make its decision based on the relevant information. If you open with a yes or no then counsel has got the answer they want, they'll cut you off as you speak and they'll move past the point. You will have lost the opportunity to clarify. On that point, don't rely on your side to be able to come back and fix it up or give you a chance to clarify; they may either have been thinking about something else or they may miss the point of what your clarification will add to their case — you're the witness, not them.

3   If there is a jury, don't have lingering eye contact with anyone on it.

4   When giving evidence, always direct your answer to the trier of fact, which will usually be either a judge or jury. As a witness you're there for the benefit of the court so your answers should be addressed to the court. It's a useful tactic because you can use it to break problematic or aggressive overtones when being cross-examined. If you think about it, most fights break out as the result of over-extended eye contact (usually between alpha males). If you believe the old story, looking an angry dog in the eye will get you savaged. It's the same with opposing legal counsel.

5   Always be serious. Court is a serious place. Everyone else is taking it seriously, so should you. After all, we're here to decide something that will affect people for the

rest of their lives. What an expert does at court must therefore be beyond reproach. The trier of fact has the ultimate decision to make and it must be the right and correct decision. If the wrong decision is made for whatever reason, the expert needs to be sure that their part at least was right and correct.

6   Ensure you are very clear about whether or not you have been released from your duty and are free to go. This is particularly relevant if the court takes a break. In England, court starts in the morning, runs until the lunch break and then runs until the end of play, which basically means two sessions of court time. In New Zealand, court starts in the morning, has a break for morning tea, runs until lunch time, has a lunch break, runs until afternoon tea then finishes up a bit later on, resulting in essentially four sessions. It's more civilised in that you know a break will be along soon but it also means you need to be alert about your status when a break starts — are you required to come back afterwards or have they finished with you?

One particular court occasion springs to mind in which I had given my main evidence, I'd been cross-examined by the other side and been re-examined by my barrister. I'd even answered questions from the judge. Lunch time came along and I was stood down. It was a little unclear from what was said but I assumed I'd been released, so I went over the road and settled into a café. Two o'clock rolled around and I was having lunch and a chat with some friends. Next thing I know

I get a phone call from the court asking, very politely, where the hell was I, the court's waiting for my return! Shit! Your worst nightmare as an expert — the court's waiting, it's raining outside, you have to go back for more and you've allowed your brain to think about something other than this case.

Well, all I can say is that the looks on the jurors' faces said it all as I puffed back up to the witness box with my hair awry and damp. And all they did was ask me to read two lines of evidence from earlier in the trial.

Be warned. Life as an expert witness is not glam and the court experience is a curly one.

Chapter 8

The perpetual case of drinking

I received a call from a solicitor one day and after the opening pleasantries were over he said, 'I have a client who's been charged with drink driving. She was stopped by the police after she drove out of the airport when she'd just returned from a trip to the States to get breast implants.' And that's all he said. I was waiting for him to add some details about what she might have slugged from her duty free while she was waiting the usual interminable time at passport control but no, nothing else was offered. So I said, 'And what happened next?' to which he replied, 'Nothing. That's it.'

Her whole defence to drink driving was that she'd had new boobs in the USA and they were the reason for her being over the drink-drive limit. Now, to every woman (and, in some circumstances, men) out there with new boobs, this is not a defence to drink driving. The breath reading was over the legal limit not because her new boobs were filled with brandy but because she'd got sloshed on the free booze in business class. No defence.

Same goes for pickled onions. Eating five pickled onions from the jar on the counter in the chippy will not put you over the drink-drive limit; it'll be the 10 pints of lager you had in the pub before you had a punch-up and a kebab on the way back to the car.

So far, I've not really talked much about how forensic science is applied once the theory's been learnt, so here we go. I'm going to start with a personal favourite of mine, alcohol. Before we all get confused, this is not a breakdown of my drinking habits — I am the mother of two relatively young children and I run a small business; there is no time for relaxation unless it involves 10 minutes of crime novel reading followed by sleep.

This chapter is more about how alcohol crops up in casework, how we deal with it as forensic scientists and what it all means. After all, alcohol is a hugely popular drug. The ancient Egyptians were kind enough to leave behind pictographs showing the use of wine around 6000 years ago. There is also suggestion that Neolithic people were fermenting alcohol and had stone beer jugs, which would put the use of alcohol as far back as 9000 years ago, during the time period to which geologists and archaeologists refer as the Holocene.

Most parents worry that the 'youth of today' are starting to drink alcohol younger and younger, and they should be very worried. A 1997 study involving data from more than 27,500 current and former drinkers in the USA showed that 40 per cent of adults who started drinking at or before the age of 14 developed a lifetime dependence, compared with only 10 per cent if they start drinking at 20 or older. Unfortunately, alcohol is so socially acceptable that it's a major contributor in a significant proportion of crimes, often drink driving or those crimes to which we refer as 'crimes against the person' — sometimes they're one and the same. In New Zealand, as

I understand it, alcohol is a factor in a quarter of all traffic offences, a third of violence (including domestic) cases and half of all serious violence cases. You just have to take a look down your local high street on a Saturday night to see what I mean — it's everywhere and, dare I say it, New Zealand is a hard-drinking nation.

We are, as a society, extremely reliant on our motor vehicles; the idea of not being able to drive for nine months, 12 months, or even longer, is more than we can bear. Some people will lose their jobs and, potentially, their homes if they lose their driving licence. For this reason, many people choose to defend a charge of drink driving but the question of defending oneself is occasionally asked. My favourite answer comes from an Auckland-based barrister who reassures potential clients that, yes, you can indeed be convicted, sentenced and jailed completely free of charge. If you want help navigating the technicalities that are a drink-drive defence, perhaps legal advice should be sought.

In forensic casework, we look at how alcohol may have influenced a sequence of events that leads to the eventual 'event of interest'. It could be something as relatively insignificant as someone moving their car 10 metres down the road after they've had a few drinks and clipping next door's Ford Fiesta while they're parallel parking, or it could be something far more extreme, such as a drug and alcohol-fuelled frenzy, which results in someone being kicked to death.

In all cases we have to consider several things, including the pattern of alcohol consumption (such as what was drunk and at what times), what time the crime/incident occurred, the drinker's vital statistics (height, weight, gender — age can also be taken into consideration), any medication, what the driver might have eaten and how used they were to drinking alcohol. We undertake several sets of calculations to work out the blood alcohol concentration people achieve after drinking. At the time of writing, New Zealand law stipulates the drink-driving limit as being 400 micrograms of alcohol per litre of breath or 80 milligrams of alcohol per 100 millilitres of blood, although there are rumblings about lowering the limit to 50 in blood (and a corresponding reduction in the breath limit).

If you're under 20 years old, the figures are 150 micrograms of alcohol per litre of breath and 30 milligrams of alcohol per litre of blood. These numbers relate to how much alcohol is travelling around in the blood at the time the needle enters a vein for a sample to be taken, or how much alcohol is in the breath when someone breathes into one of those nice pieces of testing kit at the police station. In England and Wales, providing a urine sample is also an option but it can complicate matters from the calculation perspective because of all sorts of issues around how long since the person last had a wee, whether the sample was collected in accordance with certain procedures, and so on.

The blood/breath (and urine) alcohol calculations follow the original work of a Swedish scientist, Erik Widmark, whose seminal work was published in the 1930s and then translated into English. Much work has been done since then in order to refine the accuracy of the calculations, and a lot of that additional work has used data from actual drivers and casework, as well as data from study groups.

The most common calculation converts the alcohol in the glass into alcohol in the body. By this I mean it converts the alcohol in, say, a bottle of beer into a blood alcohol concentration for a particular person. For example, a stubbie of Mac's Gold contains 330 millilitres (ml) of alcoholic beverage of which the alcohol makes up four per cent of the volume. This is what '4% ABV' (or 'alcohol by volume') means on the side of the bottle. Four per cent of 330 ml is 13.2 ml so 13.2 ml of the total volume is made up of alcohol. When this is converted to actual grams of alcohol, this is 10.43 grams. So there are 10.43 grams of alcohol in an average bottle of Mac's Gold (give or take the variation allowed during the brewing process, but that's a different story). If my brother drank that Mac's Gold, it would contribute about 14 milligrams of alcohol to every 100 millilitres of his blood. If I drank it, it would contribute about 25 milligrams of alcohol per 100 millilitres of my blood. The difference is because he is male, 6 foot four and about 18 stone (114 kilograms, unless he's been on a diet recently) whereas I am female, 5 foot 8 and about 9½ stone (60 kilograms).

You can easily see that if we drank several of these each, I would be over the blood alcohol limit for driving far quicker than him and it would also take longer for me to drop below the legal limit again because I would have a higher concentration of alcohol in my blood — I'm smaller by volume, I therefore have less space into which to distribute the same volume of alcohol, ergo my blood alcohol concentration will be greater. When it comes to alcohol concentration, the human body is like a big bag of water. If you pour a cup of blue dye into a small bag of water, the dye will be more concentrated than if the same volume of dye is poured into a big bag of water — it's the same principle with people.

There are two separate processes to consider when talking about the fate of alcohol in the body (that is, what happens to it when it's inside you): absorption and elimination. Absorption is all about how the alcohol is soaked into the blood; elimination is about how the body gets rid of the alcohol once it's been soaked up. People often get these two processes mixed up but they're separate, even though the time they occur overlaps.

Absorption is what happens to the alcohol once it is poured into the mouth and flows on into the gastric region — the stomach and small intestine. For the years I worked in England, alcohol cases were always considered without much regard for whether or not someone had been drinking on an empty stomach, but it does make a difference and there's now plenty of scientific literature to support that view.

What seems to be at issue is what sort of food has the greatest effect on absorption of the alcohol. It's not rocket science — anyone who drinks even occasionally will know that whether or not they drink on an empty stomach will affect how they feel after they've had a few drinks. This is because alcohol is absorbed more quickly from the small intestine than it is from the stomach. When alcohol is poured down the throat, the first place it can rest for a period of time is the stomach. If someone is eating or has eaten before they start drinking alcohol, the valve at the end of the stomach (the pyloric sphincter) shuts. Imagine it a bit like a little door that closes when there's food in the stomach. Closing the door keeps the alcohol in the stomach. The role of the stomach is to contain the food and break it down into a mushy paste using various chemicals and enzymes. If there is no food in the stomach, the door at the far end is open, the alcohol can pour into the stomach and then out again through the door and into the small intestine. Alcohol is more readily absorbed from the small intestine than from the stomach, which means the effects can be felt more quickly.

Most people are aware of this — I'm sure I'm not alone when I say I've heard *many* stories of people getting drunk and, generally speaking, they became drunk more quickly and felt more drunk when they drank on an empty stomach. There's the old wife's tale of lining your stomach with milk before you drink — I assume this works because it causes the pyloric sphincter 'door' to close, thus containing the alcohol to the stomach and therefore slowing down absorption.

Scientific opinion is that there is an optimal strength and bubbliness of alcoholic beverage that maximises absorption. This is equivalent to a standard gin and tonic. Having said that, what is standard? A standard measure of spirit in England and Wales is 25 ml, in New Zealand it's 35 ml. In England and Wales if you ask for a G and T you'll get 25 ml of gin plus some tonic; in New Zealand you'll get 70 ml of gin plus some tonic because double measures are poured as standard but in England and Wales you get a single measure. Awareness of variation is the key to safe drinking when you're overseas.

Elimination of alcohol is how the body gets rid of it by metabolising it (breaking it down), largely in the liver. The rate of elimination varies across the general population but is largely independent of height, weight and gender. Once alcohol has been absorbed, it moves around the body in the bloodstream and when it encounters the liver, it starts being removed through the process of metabolism. The process of elimination starts within a few minutes of someone starting to drink alcohol and the rate at which it is eliminated is pretty constant until the blood alcohol levels get quite low, after which it tails off.

How alcohol makes a person feel is a different matter. Although the amount of alcohol in the blood is directly related to how much alcohol someone has consumed, how drunk someone gets, feels and appears is sometimes unpredictable, especially when other drugs are involved. However, it's accepted that after alcohol consumption and absorption, people follow a general trend in behaviour and these trends can be related to blood alcohol concentrations. After the first drink, and assuming it's a standard drink and not a yard of ale, many people won't really notice any effect and outwardly they appear just fine. This is the stage when, legally (in New Zealand and the United Kingdom anyway) people are still allowed to drive, with their blood alcohol concentration generally between 10 and 50; several countries in central and eastern Europe have a zero tolerance rule, whereby alcohol consumption means no driving. It has the immediate virtue of being really easy to understand and implement.

After the stage of 'no real effects' or 'subclinical', behaviour tends to range into mild euphoria, sociability and talkativeness followed by increased confidence, decreased inhibitions accompanied by reduced attention and judgement with some sensory and motor skill impairment and a reduced rate of information processing. Once your blood alcohol level is causing the latter sorts of effects, you definitely shouldn't be driving, from either a legal perspective or a practical one. This is the 'euphoria' stage (blood alcohol concentration between 30 and 120, legal limit currently being 80). The blood alcohol limit for driving straddles the subclinical and euphoria stages.

The 'excitement' stage is characterised by impaired balance, a reduction in coordination leading to staggering or erratic gait, possible nausea, poor sensory perception, drowsiness and an increase in the time it takes to react to an external stimulus. This and the euphoria stage, in my professional experience, are the stages at which most drunk drivers are likely to think that driving is still a good idea. Blood alcohol levels of between about 90 and 250 occur during this stage.

The 'confusion' stage (blood alcohol levels between about 180 and 300) involves dizziness, 'drunkenness' as we know it and disorientation — when you're having trouble getting the key in the front door. Apathy, increased drowsiness and lethargy are also common — so you're likely to pass out when you hit a horizontal surface, whether it be the pavement or your bed. You also might experience an increased pain threshold so you don't notice when you bang your head on the curbstone, and vision disturbances.

The stage before 'coma' and 'death' is 'stupor' (blood alcohol range approximately 250 to 400) in which you are about to lose your motor functions and you are unable to stand or walk as a result of muscular in-coordination. You might pass out and/or suffer incontinence.

Once you've reached 'coma' stage (blood alcohol levels in the region of 350 to 500), there's unconsciousness possibly associated with depressed or unresponsive reflexes, reduced blood circulation and reduced ability to breathe. Your temperature falls as you approach the health danger limit and death is now a distinct possibility. Eventually, your blood is so soaked with alcohol you are unable to control your muscles and you can't breathe. You are dying but you probably don't know about it because you're unconscious. When your blood alcohol level clocks over 450, there's a good chance you're dead.

To accompany the suggestion of lowering the drink-driving level in New Zealand, there has been much comment in the media about the effects (or not) of a related reduction in drink-driving 'accidents'. The road traffic police in England refer to them as 'avoidable incidents', because they are; there's nothing accidental about them. Personally, I think that although a reduction in the drink-drive limit would not immediately and dramatically reduce the number of road traffic incidents in which alcohol is a factor, time would make its mark. Drink driving is socially acceptable in New Zealand, more so than in other countries. Kiwis drink hard and long. Peer pressure in my age group (currently late thirties/early forties) that reduced drink driving in England and Wales during the 1980s and 1990s does not exist to the same degree here.

People often seem to drink and drive in this country because there is the general perception that the driver can 'calculate' what they can get away with drinking before they are over the limit. By the time they are over the limit, they are in the 'euphoria' stage and, in my experience, mostly in the 'excitement' stage. Personally, I wonder whether the current law is fair in allowing an individual, who is probably already impaired to drive, to make a sensible decision about whether or not they're impaired to drive. I realise that lowering the blood alcohol limit to 50 is the top end of the subclinical stage but the effects of alcohol vary within and between individuals, regardless of the limit stipulated by the law.

In that regard, alcohol is a unique drug — no other drug has a level stipulated in law for driving precisely because the effects of drugs are unpredictable and are complicated by mixing of drugs (including alcohol), people's habituation and other factors. Regardless, I will carry on doing calculations based on the limit of 80 because that is what the law says. Alcohol is a major contributor to so many other crimes in this country — it's never going to go away.

As with everything, though, these things are never straight-forward and there are always exceptions to the rule. Alcoholics spring to mind. Most people think that alcoholics can take their beer better than the rest of us and in many instances that's true, but it doesn't make it a good thing. The bodies of alcoholics have often adapted to the continual supply of large amounts of alcohol and their livers can eliminate alcohol at a quicker-than-average rate. The person is also often used to the effects of alcohol so can function with blood alcohol levels so high the rest of us would be falling down flat or giggling like teenagers with a bottle of bubbly.

This kind of argument has often been used in drink-driving cases where the driver says that they are an alcoholic and metabolise alcohol faster than normal. The gist of the request from the lawyer in these cases is that any blood alcohol calculations I might make should not use the average rate of elimination but should use the fastest rates of elimination. This means the driver's blood alcohol level would fall to the legal limit sooner than an average member of the public because they get rid of the alcohol from their bodies much more quickly.

At this point I should mention that there are clinical/

medical descriptions that clarify the differences between social, heavy and dependent drinkers and alcoholics. I don't intend to go into those definitions because my job doesn't involve having to discern the difference, although I do take into account a person's drinking history. The other reason for not going into detailed descriptions is that such groupings are best used by the people who defined them; generally speaking, I work with people who use phrases like 'heavy drinker' and 'alcoholic' interchangeably. I also work with people who want to demonstrate extremes to suit their case (and I'm not necessarily talking about lawyers) and they will use medical terms to suit their needs. By avoiding such terms and just describing the circumstances that relate to a particular case, I avoid falling into traps regarding descriptions.

The eventual effect of continuous excess alcohol consumption is that the liver can't take it any more and slows down its processing, because it's damaged. This means the alcohol remains in the body for longer. Many alcoholics have a residual blood alcohol level, so after a night out on the pop, they carry over alcohol in their bloodstream to the next day and then they start drinking again, adding to their blood alcohol level. I expect many of them never reach a zero alcohol level. It's worth remembering that these aren't necessarily the people you see sleeping on park benches. It's just as likely to be someone who drinks a lot every evening yet can still get up and function seemingly normally the next day — it's just what the body becomes used to. The real problems for them would start when they reduced their intake and their body would have to readjust, which, as anyone who knows someone who's gone dry, is a tough process.

Compared with England and Wales, drink-driving cases in New Zealand are relatively straightforward. Generally speaking, if you are stopped by the cops and you're over the drink-drive limit, you're guilty on the basis of a conclusive presumption, which means that your level at the time of the offence is taken to be the same as the reading that shows up on the blood/breath-testing device. In New Zealand, there is pretty much no way to challenge the breath or blood alcohol result.

New Zealand law is tempered somewhat by the ability to apply for a limited licence (also known as a work licence). If you are granted one of these then you can carry on driving, but with limitations. Legal grounds for such a licence are that if you are not granted one, you will suffer extreme hardship, or your family will suffer undue hardship.

In England and Wales there is no such luxury. However, there are three defences to drink driving written in to the Road Transport Act 1988. These are post-incident alcohol consumption, also referred to as the 'hip flask defence', spiked drinks and Drunk In Charge. For the lawyers among you, the legislation reads:

Driving or being in charge of a motor vehicle with alcohol concentration above prescribed limit

(1) If a person a) drives or attempts to drive a motor vehicle on a road or other public place or, b) is in charge of a motor vehicle on a road or other public place, after consuming so much alcohol that the proportion of it in his breath, blood or urine exceeds the prescribed limit he is guilty of an offence.

(2) It is a defence for a person charged with an offence under (1)b) above to prove that at the time he is alleged to have committed the offence the circumstances were such that there was no likelihood of his driving the vehicle while the proportion of alcohol in his breath, blood or urine remained likely to exceed the prescribed limit.

A lot of readers may have just skated over that last bit but in order to fully understand the law, please read it again. Then remember that there is an important assumption made by the law — that for the purposes of defending a drink-driving charge, the amount of alcohol in the driver's body at the time of the incident will be taken to be not less than that recorded by the evidential specimen of breath, blood or urine.

To make that last bit mean something, a practical example of that would be Mr Smith, who drank 10 pints of beer, got into his car and tried to drive home. He drove into a wall at 11.30 p.m., stalled the car, couldn't get it started again and decided he'd make a surreptitious escape and because he's drunk, thinks no one will ever know it was him — forgetting that he's left the car behind. The police come along on a routine patrol, find the car, establish no one's in it and find the address of the registered owner. They pop along to Mr Smith's house and find him asleep on the lawn. Mr Smith wakes up, provides a positive sample of breath to a handheld alcohol-screening device and is assisted to the police station. Once at the police station, he provides a sample of blood. The sample is analysed and found to contain not less than 100 milligrams of alcohol per 100 millilitres of blood — the legal limit is 80 so he's potentially guilty of drink driving. The Crown will prosecute Mr Smith on the basis that his blood alcohol level at the time he provided the blood sample was not less than 100 and that his level at the time he crashed into the wall was therefore also not less than 100.

Drunk In Charge

Number (2) in the bit of legislation I quoted previously is commonly referred to as being charged with DIC and it's the easiest one to deal with. Basically, if a person drives into town, goes out on the pop, drinks all their taxi money, decides not to drive home (very good) but instead goes to sleep in the car until they wake up, they can still be charged with being DIC. Even if the keys are not about their person or if they are asleep in the back seat with the car keys in their pocket, they can be guilty of this offence.

At first glance this might seem a bit harsh. Think about it, though. The chances are that although the driver starts off with a good intention (not drinking and driving), they'll wake up in the car after a few hours' kip (or unconsciousness), cramped, thirsty, uncomfortable, wanting their bed and, most likely, still over the legal drink-drive limit. Lots of people drink drive on Saturday and Sunday mornings because they're still over the limit from a big booze-up the night before, particularly if they drink into the early hours.

The way drivers can avoid being found guilty of this offence is by saying that, had they not been arrested by the nice policeman who tapped on the window at 3 a.m. in the local car park, they wouldn't have driven their vehicle home until their breath/blood/urine alcohol level was below the legal limit. They then have to say at what time they would have driven.

After that, it's over to someone like me who does some simple calculations to determine whether or not the individual would have been above or below the legal limit at the time the driver says they would have driven. It doesn't take a brain surgeon to work out that if the driver picks a time distant enough in the future, their breath/blood/urine alcohol level will be zero, never mind under the legal limit. The problem with that is credibility and the key word in the legislation is *likelihood*. The magistrates (because these cases are usually dealt with by the lower courts) generally have a tough time believing that Mr Smith, who was found slumped over the steering wheel of his Nissan Micra in the pub car park at 4.30 in the morning, wouldn't have dreamt of driving the 30 miles home for another 17 hours if he hadn't been arrested by the police. Everyone in the courtroom knows there was a very strong likelihood he would have woken up when he became cold, started the engine and probably got home by about seven, just in time for a nice hangover-repelling fry-up breakfast.

I prepared dozens of reports for cases like this and I can only remember one that I thought had a snowball's chance of being successful. Remember I prepare reports based on the instructions provided to me, regardless of whether my report will be helpful or not. Whether my report is used is a decision for the defendant and the lawyer, not me.

This particular case involved a guy who was staying at his mate's place one Saturday night. The driver parked his car on the grass verge outside the house, so legally it was still on the public highway. His mate's parents didn't like smoking in the house and it was raining so while they had a few beers before walking to the local pub, which was 500 metres down the road, they sat in the car for a cigarette and a drink. The key was in the ignition so they could listen to the stereo but the engine wasn't on because the car was fitted with an immobiliser that required a separate key, the key being in the house in the car owner's overnight bag where he left it because he wasn't going to be driving. He kept the ignition key and the immobiliser key on separate keyrings because he'd previously had a car stolen as the result of him putting both keys on the same keyring.

The police came along, breathalysed the driver and he was, surprise surprise, over the legal limit, so he was charged with being DIC. This case actually went to court where several witnesses were called for the defence, including the driver/defendant, a garage mechanic and me. The Crown Prosecution Service would not drop the case and insisted that it be tried. It was tried and the defendant was found not guilty: the magistrates basically asked how the defendant could possibly have had any intention of driving the car when it required an immobiliser to work and the immobiliser was in the house? Why would he have had any need to drive home when he was staying the night?

Let's now look at the two defences I mentioned earlier, the hip flask defence and the spiked drinks defence.

Hip flask defence

The hip flask defence is the term for post-incident alcohol consumption, which relates to those cases where, for example, someone crashed their car then nipped home and had a large snifter of brandy before the police arrived. They then claim the reason their breath alcohol level was over the legal limit was not because they'd drunk five glasses of wine with their restaurant dinner prior to driving home, but because of the brandy they had to steady their nerves after the crash.

This is an extremely popular defence and there are many, many examples of its use. For magistrates hearing these cases on a regular basis, it got to be a bit like the dog-ate-my-homework story — new and apparently convincing to the student, old hat and totally unbelievable to the teacher. However, as with all these things, some cases do stand out and there was one in particular I remember. Not only did I feel sorry for the defendant, and I never usually have any feelings one way or the other — that's my job — but I actually believed what he was saying, not that I said that to anyone: that's *not* my job.

In this case, I had to attend court to give evidence, which meant I heard the trial proceedings, including the defendant giving evidence. It transpired that the defendant's car was found parked across the corner of a road junction, partly on the grass, partly on the road. His wife had skipped off to shack up with his best mate and had taken the children with her, without telling the defendant where she was going or that she was taking the children. The defendant drove round to the new fella's house in case that's where they were. It was Saturday and there was nowhere to park down this small residential road because everyone was at home, so he just ditched the car where he thought it would be OK and stormed off to the house to confront his wife (or, probably more accurately, his ex-wife). When he got there, the wife refused to let him see the children and threatened to call the police and have him removed if he didn't leave. Not wanting to upset the children by making a big show, the defendant left, feeling rattled and angry. Rather than going home, he walked up the road to the local pub where he drank seven pints of strong beer. He said he intended to get a taxi home. The police walked into the pub while Mr Defendant was on his seventh pint and asked if anyone owned the illegally parked car on the corner. The defendant confirmed it was his, was arrested and then charged with drink driving. What would have helped his case was the landlord of the pub giving evidence to say he had served the defendant and that he hadn't been drunk when he'd arrived in the pub. Unfortunately, the landlord was a friend of the wife's new bloke, so no support there.

I don't normally wait in court to hear the outcome of a case because, professionally speaking, the outcome is of no significance — I'm there for the benefit of the court and when they've finished with me, they tell me so and I can leave, so I do. On this occasion, I had to have words with the barrister before I left court because there was some dispute between the bean counters at the court and my employer about who had said I should attend and therefore who would be paying the bill for my attendance — if you leave the court before getting that sort of thing sorted out then the English courts will never pay and neither will your instructing solicitor.

The upshot was that it all turned to custard for the defendant, he was found guilty and lost his driving licence. The worst part was that he couldn't see his children — he worked odd hours and the bus service to where his children were living was non-existent; he had to wait until he'd served his ban before he could see them, which was a mandatory 12 months (down to nine months if he took a court-approved Drink Driving

Awareness course). He was in tears when the magistrates sentenced him. It was terrible. I was so disheartened when I left — and, as far as I know, the court never did pay for my attendance. The company never did any more cases heard in that court, which was good, because it was a shocker of a concrete grey box with orange, hard-seated plastic chairs and the worst tea machine south of London.

Spiked/laced drinks

The other defence to drink driving is the spiked drinks defence. These are the cases where people say, for example, that they only drank two pints of beer before driving home after an evening in the pub and were stopped by the police at a checkpoint only to find they were over the legal limit. Their argument is that someone at the pub must have added two double measures of vodka to each of their pints of beer without their knowledge. The problem with these cases was that usually the additional alcohol was apparently added by someone at the bar, usually a stranger, when the drinks were ordered. The thing is that pint glasses usually require filling to the top to be a pint, so where does the extra volume of liquid fit? Does the spiker slurp out a great mouthful of beer first before adding the vodka? If so, why doesn't the drink owner notice while they're paying for their drinks?

There are variations on the theme of course, which were particularly prevalent after Christmas — the brandy-in-the-Christmas-pudding or sherry-in-the-trifle. Sherry in the trifle deserves some consideration because trifles aren't baked (not usually, but anything's possible in my experience), although there was one case where allegedly an entire bottle (700 ml) of cherry brandy was added to a trifle and the defendant ate half of the entire trifle. Anyone who has made a trifle will know that if too much liquid is added, it turns into a multi-coloured stream of sprinkles, cream and jelly. In that case, I think the magistrates 'formed a view' that it wasn't really very plausible.

Brandy on the Christmas pudding or wine in the casserole is never a flyer because these food items are heated. Alcohol evaporates very easily, particularly when heated. In fact, the whole point of pouring brandy over the Christmas pudding is to set fire to it, thus burning off the alcohol. Still, I guess people think it's worth a go.

In addition to the defences allowed by the law there are people who'll give anything a go, just in case it might get them off a drink-drive charge. Here are some of my favourites from over the years from various countries.

I had a case once where a biker had been involved with some road traffic incident or other and he had been taken back to a police station 'for the purposes of providing an evidential breath sample, blood sample or both'. The breath-testing device wasn't working so he was required, by law, to provide a blood sample. He said he couldn't give a sample of blood because he had a profound fear of needles. In such circumstances, the police could have chosen to ask him to provide a urine sample instead but they didn't exercise this option because they'd taken a look at this chap, seen he was plastered in tattoos and decided there was no way he was needle phobic. Because the defendant refused to give a blood sample and the police refused to offer a urine sample, the defendant was charged with Failing to Provide a Sample for Analysis.

I received a phone call from the solicitor asking what I could do about it. I advised that although as a forensic scientist I couldn't do anything, I was aware that having a tattoo needle hammering into the skin isn't the same as having a needle inserted into a vein for the collection of a blood sample. With needle phobia it's not just the action of the needle in the skin, it's the psychological aspect as well, which is often the thing with which people seem to struggle. Phobias are often irrational.

I suggested the solicitor seek a professional medical opinion, which he did. The case came to trial and the defendant was successful because the medic distinguished between needles involved in having a tattoo and the manner in which a blood sample is taken from a vein. Maybe the defendant had been drink driving, but he wasn't guilty of Failing to Provide because he had a real medical condition that precluded giving a blood sample. If only the police had asked him to pee in a pot.

Here's an interesting one, an English case. Solicitor calls. Their client is a Jehovah's Witness who failed a breath-screening test, which means alcohol was detected in a breath sample he blew into a roadside-screening device that is extremely reliable in detecting alcohol — if the test showed a fail then the driver has consumed so much alcohol he's over the legal limit to drive. The police station breath-testing device wasn't working so the driver was required to provide a blood sample. He refused on religious grounds. The driver was required to provide a urine sample. He refused on religious grounds. Can I help? My response: why did the defendant fail a breath-screening test when he wasn't supposed to have been drinking alcohol to excess anyway, as drunkenness is forbidden as part of the same set of religious beliefs he was quoting? Seems to me he was being a mite selective in applying the tenets of his faith. Human beings eh? We'll try anything!

A common misconception is that a woman's menstrual cycle somehow affects her blood alcohol level, and there has been specific research to address exactly this issue. It's also a well-known fact that women's moods can change, sometimes rapidly, at various parts of their cycle and I remember some research shown as part of a TV programme that assessed whether diet made any difference. Apparently, it does — eating dairy products at certain stages through the month can reduce the effects of mood swings, although they won't necessarily get rid of them altogether. But can the menstrual cycle, on its own, adversely affect a woman's blood alcohol level? In a word, no. It just affects how you feel, not the actual numerical blood alcohol concentration.

There is a defence to drink driving I encountered several times in England and Wales, not actually directly related to the drink-driving offence as defined in the Road Traffic Act, but in relation to the ability to provide a sample of breath for analysis. If someone refuses to provide a sample of breath for analysis, they can be charged with Failing to Provide. However, there were many occasions when someone said that they hadn't refused; they were just too drunk to be able to coordinate their lungs to provide a satisfactory sample. I remember one Christmas when we had our work's Christmas do and one of the group drank a lot of wine, probably followed by a chaser of some sort. We used to take the handheld breath tester along with us to see how accurate the breath alcohol calculations were. You have to ask how sad is it that our idea of fun at a work party was to calculate our breath alcohol levels, but there you go, that's scientists for you. Anyway, that particular year my colleague tried to blow into the breath tester but was so drunk he just couldn't do it. He really tried but he had totally lost the ability to coordinate his mouth and lungs for the time required to provide a satisfactory sample. The point of the story is that he genuinely wouldn't have been able to provide a satisfactory breath sample to either a handheld screening device or an evidential device, similar to the ones they have at the police station. Although he would technically have been guilty of Failing to Provide a Breath Sample, should the fact he was too drunk be a defence? Most judges think not. And, yes, we all took taxis home.

Petrol consumption is a defence that's cropped up a few times, mostly by people who don't realise that drinking petrol tends to trigger the body's vomit reflex, thus expelling said petrol and any alcohol remaining in the stomach. The police are often interested in people who have been drinking petrol, just in case the petrol was being drunk from a vehicle other than the driver's own.

There have also been several cases involving gas stoves in camping situations. The version of events is something along the lines of the gas bottle needing to be changed but it let out a bit of gas during the change and because the person was in a tent at the time, which was an enclosed space, they inhaled the gas and it adversely affected their blood alcohol level. The main issue the courts seem to have with this is that the campers have usually been drinking the night before, they've got up early the next day because that's what happens when you camp — donkeys and cockerels and such like insisting on marking the start of the day in some inhumanely vociferous manner at the crack of dawn, and need to go to the shop for some reason. Unfortunately, these campers tend to be carrying over a bit of last night's alcohol in their blood supply, which is the reason for being over the drink-drive limit — nothing to do with gas canisters. In fact, at least one police force I know of used to stop campers on their way home from picturesque forest locations on a Sunday morning because they knew very well they'd have a pretty good hit rate on drivers over the legal limit.

New sweets on the market (or sometimes even old favourites) were usually a pretty fair bet for a drink-drive defence. Extra strong mints, Victory V lozenges, the sort of chewing gum that has sugary liquid in the middle — all have been the subject of drink-driving defences, along with many others. The girls in the office used to love these cases because the only way to know if there was an effect was to try the sweeties of the moment and then blow into the breath-screening device. The sweeties were paid for out of petty cash and we had multiple samples because everyone wanted a go. I never managed to convince anyone that I should try it with a bar of Dairy Milk, though, which was a bit disappointing.

It's amazing the number of drink drivers who think the reason they were over the legal limit wasn't anything to do with the alcohol they poured into themselves but must be because they have a 'slow metabolism'. To be fair, statistically speaking, some people do eliminate alcohol at a lower than average rate, which means it'll take their bodies longer to eliminate a glass of wine than the next person.

For those who are very insistent on this as being a reason for drink driving, we as scientists can make an assessment of an individual's breath alcohol elimination rate. This usually involves the person in question coming in to the office to undertake some tests. The procedure has been honed to its present standard as the result of bad experiences in the past, mostly, thankfully, that occurred before my time. Back in the day, a previous colleague had such a procedure-defining case, which involved a local businessman. He was well known for having a few too many sherries at lunch time and he'd finally been caught driving with excess breath alcohol (the businessman, not my colleague). The man came in to have his breath alcohol elimination rate tested, which involves drinking a calculated quantity of vodka at about nine in the morning and then sitting around for several hours and providing breath samples to a handheld device every 30 minutes or so. Once the breath alcohol level falls below the legal limit, the subject can leave and we use the results to calculate the average breath alcohol elimination rate. The calculations will only have any meaning if we, the scientists, can be sure the subject hasn't been drinking before they arrive, and doesn't consume any more alcohol after the test has started.

To address the first possibility, we ask people to undertake a breath test before we get started, just to make sure they blow zero. In the case of this particular man, he provided a zero breath reading, as required. After he'd drunk his early morning vodka he asked if he could nip down the road to get a paper, because he hadn't realised there'd be so much sitting around with nothing much to do. My colleague, being a trusting sort, agreed and so off went the man down the road. Ten minutes passed and he hadn't returned; more time passed, no man. So my colleague went into the street to see if he could find said stray man, and there he was, round the corner, face down on the street, reeking of medication and booze. As it turns out, the man had decided he wanted his breath alcohol elimination rate to seem slower than average, so he'd brought some horse liniment in his jacket and was swigging it while he wandered off to the paper shop. Seeing as horse liniment wasn't made for human consumption, it had a bit of a bad effect on him and he passed out. My boss called an ambulance, which pretty much called a halt to the breath alcohol experiment. The testing procedures were adjusted accordingly; subjects who come for breath alcohol testing are now kept in sight the entire time they are 'in test conditions', including being accompanied to the toilet, should their need be pressing.

After many years of working in forensic science, I still maintain that alcohol-related cases are the most complicated, because of the calculations, how many things have to be taken into consideration and the sheer range of variables. However, they are also among the most interesting, because it's amazing what people do when they've been drinking.

Chapter 9

The pieman and the circus

This story starts as a common-or-garden drink-driving case. The solicitor's instructions described a defendant who was an alcoholic, in the true sense of the word. She'd driven her monstrous four-wheel-drive vehicle down a country lane at four in the afternoon while soaked to the eyeballs in lunch-time (and possibly breakfast-time) vodka. On her jolly little sojourn, she'd side-swiped a cyclist and, because of her erratic driving and general careering into hedgerows, he was able to keep up with her until she got home, which was a caravan in the garden of a burnt down house. The cyclist, being an assiduous sort, called the police and waited for them to arrive, all the while keeping an eye on the caravan and its occupant. While waiting, the cyclist saw what turned out to be the driver's daughter arriving in another vehicle, enter the caravan and then the police arrived.

In due course, I received instructions regarding what the driver said she'd drunk before driving (two glasses of wine in the pub) plus what she said she'd drunk after she got home (1½ litres of vodka in 20 minutes) before the police arrived. Based on what she said, her breath alcohol level would have been below the legal limit at the time of the driving incident, so I was asked to attend court to give evidence for the defence. This was where it got weird.

The trial was to be heard in a lovely semi-rural court with easy parking, good sandwiches and a nice jewellery shop over the road. I arrived at the appointed and standard 9.30 a.m. to find an ambulance outside. Thinking nothing of it, I made my way into the court building and made myself known to the people with the clipboards.

I then went to see if I could track down the barrister. This is often a challenge because it's not unusual to be instructed by someone I've never seen and vice versa. I eventually found a tall, solid-looking man pacing around and talking on a phone to someone about event organisation, who seemed to be insisting that yes indeed, pink champagne was a must, given the colour of the dress. Turns out that the barrister in question had a parallel career, which was apparently far more interesting than the case at hand.

After he'd finished ordering white lilies and pink carnations for a sixtieth birthday he was also organising, I asked him where the defendant was. Time was ticking on, we should be getting into court and generally speaking it's barristers who fuss about the time, not me. 'Oh,' he said casually, 'that's her in the ambulance outside. She fell over in the road on the way in — pissed.'

I was a bit shocked at this because if a person is up in court for drink driving, even the most hardened soaks try not to sup anything before the trial begins, certainly not until the lunch break, although there was another case when court security had to physically carry the defendant out of the pub after the lunch break and into the witness box to give evidence. But here was our defendant, being carried into court by the ambulance staff. I assumed they'd ship her off home or into rehab or something, but they didn't. They carried her into court and put her in the dock because she couldn't do it herself, yet astonishingly they considered she was fit to stand trial.

Next thing you know, she'd been carried out again because there was a fight in our courtroom. The case before ours involved two rival families and they were trapped in a small venue with nothing but hormones, rage and plastic seats between them. Police from a waiting riot van charged through the front door and into the courtroom, accidentally knocking over our drunken defendant who, to be honest, could have been knocked over by a strong wind. Several feuding family members were removed by the available police, but not all of the family members because there were too many. In fact, one of the family took a real dislike to the prosecutor for trying to put his brother in prison because of his anger management issues. This necessitated leaping across the courtroom, through the doors and grabbing the prosecutor in a vice-like grip around his neck in the foyer of the court. By this time, all the police officers were otherwise occupied with various relatives, so that left the court security officers — one tall, skinny and looking about 12 years old, the other one shorter and not moving fast, either by design or lack of desire.

I've often hoped no trouble would kick off in court because I don't want to see security guards take down a crazed family member. Defendants are less of a risk because they're generally contained or restrained in some way and have the focus of the police on them. I didn't hold out much hope for a timely and helpful intervention by the security guards but luckily for them, the enraged family member decided to let go of his captive, possibly as the result of the growing enlightenment of imminent arrest if he was caught doing it, or more likely because of his girlfriend kicking him in the left buttock and shrieking, 'Kev, stop it you stupid fuck — you'll get arrested. I ain't lookin' after the kids on me own wiv you in a fuckin' cell.' Kev let go.

After the feuding squabblers had been removed or left under their own steam, the prosecutor, understandably, asked for an adjournment of 30 minutes to get himself together. The defence barrister didn't challenge it, mostly because he was on the phone discussing the relative merits of strobe lights against disco lights.

It's 11 a.m. and we're finally under way. I'd asked (admittedly two hours ago) if I could sit behind defence counsel during the trial so that I could hear the relevant evidence. This is often permitted in drink-drive cases because the evidence that is heard before me is material to the calculations I undertake and the conclusions I reach. If any of the evidence is different from the instructions I used to undertake my calculations, my overall conclusions could be different, which could have a major impact on the outcome of the case, something that has happened on many occasions.

Being present in court at the very outset can be very revealing, as in this case. Defence counsel requested that the trial be adjourned to a future date on the grounds that the defendant had been found face down on the main road this very morning, not through any fault of her own but through the sheer stress of it all. The bench indicated it was disinclined to acquiesce to his request given that the matter had been adjourned several times before. Lo and behold, the cheeky bugger got up and said the previous delay had been due to his expert witness failing to submit her report on time — twice. I wouldn't mind if it had been true but I'd only been instructed three days beforehand and this case had been going on for over a year (and I've never submitted a report late). I involuntarily raised my eyebrows over the back of my head, which caught the eye of the bench who, in turn, indicated that perhaps the expert herself might have something to say about that. And I tell you, I could see from the tensing of the barrister's back muscles as the realisation washed over him from his toes to his head and back again that he'd totally forgotten I was there.

Finally, the first witness was called. It was the officer in charge of the case. I was mildly amused with his description of the argument that had taken place about the defendant's dog. When he'd arrived at the caravan, she'd insisted that her dog had to come with her to the station because it was very stressed and couldn't be left alone. The policeman had failed to see any sign of a dog but after a brief search, he and a colleague found a pile of fur that seemed to have once been some kind of animal but had the outward appearance of being dead. The defendant refused to leave without it so they actually took it with them — it had to be carried because it was unresponsive. She also had no shoes and had to be assisted to the car because she wouldn't walk on her own without shoes. There was no indication of where her shoes were or if any were ever found or even how she'd got from her car to the caravan in the first place.

The officer giving evidence was a physically rounded chap who pretty much read out his statement from his pocket notebook. I'm used to my instructing lawyers turning round to ask my opinion about something so when defence counsel turned in his seat towards me I leaned forward; I wasn't aware that the officer had said anything with which I could assist but maybe I'd missed something. I had to strain to hear what the barrister was saying, which again was not unusual. What I could finally make out was a soft, lilting rendition of *Who ate all the pies? You fat bastard, you fat bastard. Who ate all the pies? You did, you fat git.*

Many things charged through my head at that point, in no particular order:

- You're a fine one to talk, you're not so slim yourself.
- He's facing me, which is away from the bench. I'm facing the bench so I can't laugh.
- The bench thinks I'm having a serious conversation with defence counsel so I have to look serious.
- What a totally unprofessional tosser.
- Shit, I hope no one can hear this idiot singing because he's onto the second verse.

I kid you not, and it didn't end there. Next witness for the Crown was the cyclist who'd been side-swiped. After the original incident, he'd got out his paper and pen and written it all down, including times. This looked very good and he was a very credible witness, until it became apparent that he was just very slightly obsessed with this case — dates, times, names for every single court attendance, letter, communication he'd witnessed or received or made in relation to the matter, pages and pages of it committed to memory.

At the time of the incident, he'd followed the defendant and tried to talk to her at a road junction, at which point she had made it very clear (it was apparently more of a slur) that she had no interest in talking to him. I think from memory her exact words had been *piss off.* No matter, he gave his evidence and we all moved on and the rest of the Crown case passed pretty much without incident.

Then it was the turn of the defence. The barrister called the defendant's daughter to give evidence. One of the first questions was, 'What time were you in the pub with your mother?'

'About seven, we had chicken and chips for dinner,' came the answer.

I tried not to look up at anyone else, so I sneaked a peek from the corner of my eye to see what the prosecutor was going to say about that, because the police officer had just given evidence to say that he'd arrested the defendant at 4.45 p.m., two hours earlier than the daughter was now saying. The prosecutor was still visibly rattled about his near-death experience and never even noticed. The story then became even stranger, with the daughter saying her mother never drank vodka, even though the police had just produced two empty vodka bottles as evidence seized from the defendant's caravan, where she lived alone, at the time of her arrest.

When cross-examining her, my barrister asked her if she was sure about the time, to which she replied yes, and qualified it further by saying she'd heard the six o'clock news come on before she'd left the house to meet up with her mum. Sensibly, the barrister didn't push but turned round to me and said, 'We're fucked,' before promptly calling the defendant to give evidence.

Now, defendants don't have to give evidence in their own trials if they don't want to, and I was a little confused as to why the barrister would think it was a good idea, given the problems he'd had so far. His reasoning seemed to be that there was nothing left to lose and if it was this bad now, how much worse could it get? He hadn't banked on the defendant getting lost between the dock and the witness box. The defendant had been in the dock for the duration of the trial. The dock was a simple square delineated by low wooden sides and a gap where you entered or departed. There was also a bench for sitting and stairs down to the cells. When she was asked to come up to the front of the court to the witness box, she got confused and instead of coming out of the open gap, she set off down the stairs into the cells and the court clerk had to go and fetch her. Then she had trouble getting into the witness box. To be fair, it was a precarious affair, perched at the top of a set of small, tight, winding steps, but she couldn't negotiate them on her own and they were too narrow for someone to help her, so she crawled up on her hands and knees.

The details of her evidence aren't important, except that she managed a few choice words in her description of the cyclist. He, in turn, muttered constantly throughout her evidence, occasionally snorting loudly, shuffling his papers and ticking things off on what I can only assume was his timeline of events; every time she said something that must have disagreed with his list he'd mutter just loud enough to be heard but not so loud he was reprimanded.

The defendant was asked about the time she'd met her daughter in the pub and she maintained it had been lunch time, despite her own barrister pointing out that she now had the chance to adjust her account because she'd heard her daughter's evidence and perhaps the police were incorrect about their time of her arrest. According to her, no, it had definitely been lunch time, she had no memory of what her daughter had just said and, by the way, her dog was definitely alive at the time she was arrested.

At the end of her evidence, the court clerk had to go up into the witness box and prise her out, assisting her down the stairs in the same way parents do with small children who have climbed too high and scared themselves into a panic.

It was my turn after that and when I got into the witness box and looked back into the main court area, the prosecutor and bench were sitting there like stunned mullets, not sure whether to believe what was happening, the cyclist was snorting, ticking and shuffling and the defendant promptly lay down in the dock and fell asleep. After all that show, my evidence was comparatively boring.

Once I'd given my evidence and had been released, I fairly ran out of the court, because quite frankly, I had no desire to be dragged back into *The Twilight Zone.* Anyone who saw me driving home would have seen a bewildered-looking woman who spent her whole time shaking her head and saying, 'Can you believe that? Can you *believe* that just happened?'

Just out of interest, the sleepy drunk lady was found guilty. The breath readings she provided at the police station were among some of the highest I've ever encountered: 1640. The legal limit is 400. She was no more than 152 centimetres tall (about 5 foot) and weighed 38 kilograms (6 stone). The smallest ones are always the biggest worry.

Chapter 10

The case of trace

The context is often crucial to a proper interpretation.

Peter de Forest in Caddy, 2001

Once upon a time, an expensive charter vessel was moored at a wharf. Berthed close by was a scruffy trawler. The charter vessel's captain noticed that the topsides of his beautiful vessel, including the instrument mast (which, for those of a non-boating inclination, is the highest point of the vessel above sea level) were speckled with tiny brown dots of material that weren't supposed to be there. The paintwork was ruined and she needed a repaint. Who was going to pay for it? Aha! It should be the owner of the scruffy trawler because some maintenance contractors had been using an angle grinder and the swarf (the fine metallic shavings that shower like a firework when someone uses an electric cutting tool on metal) must have scattered over the nice white paintwork of the charter vessel.

Thus followed a lengthy and expensive battle about the cause of the damage — was it angle grinder swarf or was it something else?

Enter the forensic science team. I spent several chilly hours on board the charter vessel, togged up in a white, blouson scene suit but not enough in the way of thermal undergarments. To stop further damage to the boat's surfaces and also so that I didn't slip around on said surfaces, I had no shoes or socks on my feet, which didn't endear me to the occasion. By the time I got back in my car, my hands were an attractive mottled bluey orange and I was frozen to the core.

We collected specimens of the brown material and took them to the laboratory for analysis. To determine the chemistry and structure of the material, standard analytical techniques were used including scanning electron microscopy and X-ray diffraction. It turned out that the brown specks were at least in part associated with what was probably ash from the active, pluming White Island volcano in the Bay of Plenty; it later transpired the charter vessel had been fishing in the vicinity of the volcano at a time before the brown specks had been noticed.

It wasn't just the chemical analysis of trace material that solved the problem for the court. The fact that the brown flecks were found high up on the instrument mast meant that the angle grinder swarf would have to have been carried high and wide on the wind, something the court thought unlikely given the wind and tide conditions on the day in question. The court also considered it was very unlikely that the trawler's maintenance contractors would have been at work at the time when the weather conditions were right for distribution of the angle grinder swarf over the charter vessel's surfaces: 4 p.m. on a Friday afternoon. The court took the view that it was unlikely the maintenance contractors would list workaholism among their attributes.

This is a potted, limited summary of an enormously involved case that took several years, court dates and many hundreds of thousands of dollars to resolve. It's also a good example of why casework context (tides, wind speeds, working habits of cash-paid contractors) is so important in resolving issues.

Traces of all sorts of things are left behind at crime scenes. Clothes leave traces of themselves as fibres and sometimes as patterns. People leave traces of themselves as skin cells, semen, spots of blood, saliva, fingernails, ear wax and other body material. Broken windows leave traces of themselves on people's clothing and shoes as tiny fragments of glass. Cars leave traces of themselves as paint flakes or fragments of bumpers or window glass on other cars, people or items such as lampposts, trees and bicycles. Drugs leave traces of themselves as well, albeit so small they're often invisible to the naked eye. More unusual types of trace material might include soil, pollen, ash, nail polish, lipstick, oil, seed pods, sand, and as we've just seen, volcanic ash or angle grinder swarf. Basically, it includes anything that can be left behind and then later collected for analysis. The skill in applying findings from trace material often comes not just from the collecting of the sample, but also recognising what has been collected and how to get the most information from those collected samples.

If traces of material can be collected and analysed then they can be used in all kinds of casework including insurance, criminal and civil. Traces of items can be used in a number of ways: to provide associations or links between items, places and people; to provide information on circumstances using some form of reconstruction of events; or perhaps as part of an investigative approach such as determining possible provenances of samples of unknown origin.

Glass fragments are very common in casework, because they turn up in such a wide range of situations — car crashes, burglaries, car break-ins, fights and other assaults or murders involving broken bottles; the list goes on. Have a look at how much broken glass is lying around on a daily basis — near curbs, at road intersections, on main streets outside pubs and clubs, on waste ground, on beaches, in parks.

When we consider glass fragments in casework, it's not just about the circumstances of a case. Other things about the history of glass fragments have to be taken into account:

Types of glass

There's a lot of information available about different sorts of glass, what chemical compounds are added to them, how glass is manufactured, shaped and heat-treated and its various uses. Some countries manufacture glass but, as far as I'm aware, all of New Zealand's sheet glass is imported. Not all glass is created equal and there are different types: vessel glass (pint glasses, juice glasses, wine glasses and so on), domestic window glass, industrial glass (such as metal mesh reinforced glass), vehicle glass (windscreens are made of two layers of glass with a polymer layer sandwiched between them; side and rear window glass is toughened so it breaks into cubes but it's not layered) — the list is long and varied.

What happens when glass breaks

When a window or sheet of glass is broken by impact with another hard object (as opposed to just cracking through application of pressure), the majority of the glass fragments travel in the same direction as the projectile. If a brick is thrown from outside a window into a house, the brick and most of the glass shards travel into the house. However, there is also backward fragmentation of tiny glass fragments, many of which are microscopic in size. If the brick thrower is close to the window when they throw the brick then they'll be showered with tiny splinters of glass. The best forensic evidence is obtained where significant quantities of recently broken glass are found in hair combings or on the surfaces of clothing.

Persistence

Once the glass fragments have landed on our brick thrower, we have to consider how long the fragments will remain on their clothes or in their hair. People wearing woolly jumpers and jeans will retain these fragments for a relatively long period of time, particularly if they saunter away from the broken window, as opposed to running away as fast as their legs will carry them.

How much glass might be on a random member of the general population?

In order to be able to interpret scientific findings relating to glass fragments we have to understand how much glass might be found on a member of the general public. Otherwise, how will we know whether or not finding 10 glass fragments on someone is unusual? Studies have been undertaken to consider this, which also take into account where the brick thrower lives. For example, in 1970s and 1980s Northern Ireland, any member of the general public would have had more glass fragments on their clothes than someone from central New Zealand, just because of the number of bomb blasts occurring at that time.

Accidental contamination

As with any other traces, the possibility of accidental contamination should always be considered. This involves assessing how the items were seized by the police, what happened to them after they were seized and how they were examined at the laboratory.

Once we have all this information, the forensic scientist is in a position to start making sense of the circumstances of a case and what is most likely to have happened. Here are a couple of examples.

A shop window was kicked in on a Saturday night by someone walking past on the way home from the pub. Mr Spud was arrested. He said the window was already broken when he came along and all he did was go into the shop through the broken window, have a look about and come out again. He's probably broken the law in some way but is he guilty of damaging property?

The glass fragments found on his clothing confirmed he had been in the immediate vicinity of breaking or broken glass, which probably originated from the broken shop window. Did he break the window?

The glass results alone will not be able to answer this question. Glass fragments can't tell us whether or not he broke the glass or whether the fragments on his clothes got there when he walked through the freshly broken window and brushed against the glass, which would have been coated with tiny fragments. However, his downfall in this case was the fact that he was the only one seen on CCTV in the immediate vicinity at about the right time. Combining the glass results with the CCTV results was good enough for the court to convict.

In another example, sometime between 7.45 p.m. and 10.45 p.m. the side windows of two different vehicles were smashed with a brick (the first opportunity for glass fragments to be transferred onto the perpetrator) in the car park of a public house. The perpetrator then leaned into the vehicles (a Mini and a Toyota) and removed items from them (the second opportunity for glass fragments to become attached to the clothing of the perpetrator).

Mr Sheep was arrested at midnight, approximately one to four hours after the windows were smashed. Hair combings were collected and a T-shirt seized from Mr Sheep 50 minutes later. Glass samples were collected from the two damaged vehicles.

No glass was found in his hair combings; however, four fragments of fresh-looking broken glass were recovered from his T-shirt. Two of the fragments matched the broken glass from the Mini, one fragment matched the broken glass from the Toyota; the final fragment of glass originated from another source. The scientific findings provided strong support for the view that Mr Sheep had been in contact with breaking or broken glass from the broken windows of both the Mini and the Toyota.

Mr Sheep denied having broken into the two cars but said that he had spent the evening in the pub with the person who *had* broken into them. The question I was asked was whether the glass found on Mr Sheep's T-shirt could have been transferred to him from the perpetrator via a mechanism called secondary transfer. This would mean glass was transferred from the broken car window via an intermediate surface, such as the clothing of the perpetrator, onto another surface, in this case Mr Sheep's T-shirt.

In Mr Sheep's case, all four of the recovered fragments were small, being less than 0.5 millimetres in maximum dimension. The cloth of the T-shirt was reasonably good at retaining glass fragments. Given that Mr Sheep was arrested between one and four hours after the incidents occurred, he would have had to acquire the three matching glass fragments in that time period.

It was also likely that in order for three matching fragments to be recovered from his T-shirt, the number of fragments originally transferred via secondary contamination (i.e. contact with the 'contaminated' surface) would have been more than three as some will have been lost through general activity, the nature of the contact Mr Sheep had with the perpetrator and also the type of clothing being worn by that individual.

Overall, I agreed with the prosecution's expert in this case; his scientific findings had been fairly and accurately reported. Most importantly, he was correct in his assertion that Mr Sheep had probably been in contact with breaking or broken glass that originated from the Mini and the Toyota. What the prosecution's expert's statement didn't say was how the glass got onto Mr Sheep's clothing or that Mr Sheep must have been the one who broke the windows. The reason it didn't say that is because it's not possible to make that distinction on the basis of the scientific findings alone.

I then interpreted the results further based on what Mr Sheep said had happened on the night in question; that he was in the company of the perpetrator, that he had man-hugged the perpetrator when they first met, that they had sat next to each other in the velour-covered booth seats at the pub and that they had swapped seats. Having considered everything I'd been told, I couldn't exclude the possibility that transfer of three fragments had taken place by way of secondary transfer.

In yet another, more sinister example, a burglar went on a spree on a chilly winter's night, breaking into a number of properties at an industrial site. At 2.15 a.m., PC One and PC Two attended the scene.

A few streets away, Mr Unlucky left his house at around 2 a.m. to go to work. Sometime later, he was struck on the head with a metal pole and his rucksack was stolen.

At about 5 a.m. a Mr Smith was subjected to what was called a stop-and-search, which was something the police could do if they had good reason to think the person was up to something suspicious or if they fitted the profile of a criminal seen in the area. The stop-and-search was conducted by PC Three, who was assisted by PC Two and PC One, both of them back on patrol after having attended the earlier burglaries. PC One restrained Mr Smith by taking hold of his arms while PC Three conducted as thorough a search as possible given he was at the roadside. This involved a 'pat-down' of his outer clothing and visible pockets, as it seems Mr Smith wasn't very cooperative.

At the time of the stop-and-search, Mr Smith was riding a mountain bike and carrying a rucksack. He told PC Three the rucksack didn't belong to him and he'd found it in the street. As the rucksack was essentially lost property, it was seized by PC Three, but he didn't look in it.

Mr Unlucky was found in the street by a pedestrian and, after receiving the call over his police radio, PC Three attended the scene. At about 5.30 a.m. he administered first aid to Mr Unlucky, including cardiopulmonary resuscitation (CPR) and he also searched through the injured man's clothing to try to find some form of identification. Mr Unlucky was taken to hospital, accompanied by PC Three. After Mr Unlucky died, PC Three took possession of Mr Unlucky's clothes and took them back to the police station.

Once it was known that glass might be an issue in the case, PC Three gave in his stab vest and work shirt at the end of his shift so they could be examined for glass fragments.

A hooded top belonging to Mr Smith was seized two days after the night of the burglaries and the attack on Mr Unlucky. Dozens of fragments of glass were recovered from the top. Five glass fragments were recovered from Mr Unlucky's clothes, which matched glass from Mr Smith's clothing. Samples of glass from the burgled premises were examined and matched glass that had been found on Mr Smith, Mr Unlucky and PC

Three. The police were suspicious that maybe Mr Smith had been involved in the burglaries and then the attack on Mr Unlucky. Initially, the fact that PC Three had attended to Mr Unlucky was unfortunate for the police, because it wasn't possible to tell whether PC Three had transferred the glass to Mr Unlucky (which would mean that Mr Smith might not have transferred glass to the deceased) or if PC Three acquired glass fragments from Mr Unlucky (putting Mr Smith back at the scene of the murder). The rucksack recovered from Mr Smith had belonged to Mr Unlucky. So had he really found it in the street or had he been Mr Unlucky's attacker?

The glass work in this case was quite complicated, so I'm not going to précis it. Take it from me that the critical issues were not only the number of glass fragments recovered from each individual but the physical and chemical properties of those glass fragments, as well as the order of events. Mr Smith was eventually found guilty of burglary and manslaughter.

Moving on from case examples to modern policing of crimes involving glass, police in England have developed a 'crime scene kit' to give to bar and pub owners to collect glass samples after drunken brawls. Glassings or bottlings, when a glass or bottle is smashed before being thrust into the victim, often in the face, are a common occurrence in British society, usually after 10 pints of lager and shortly before a kebab on a Saturday night.

The biggest problem with cases of this type is that witnesses are often drunk and can't really remember what happened, the CCTV footage isn't always clear and the glass used in the event is usually crushed and then swept up because, obviously, it's dangerous. In cases where broken glass is successfully recovered, the scientific results can be very good — fingerprints can demonstrate the manner in which a bottle was held (bearing in mind that the neck of the bottle is often the strongest part), DNA from blood can show whose body said weapon was used against but, too often, this type of information is lost in the aftermath.

Police in Plymouth, Devon, have decided to try to combat the problem of lost evidence by handing out clean dustpan and brush kits to local pub and bar owners so they can collect the 'evidence' for later examination.

To me, this could go one way or the other. On the one hand, it's good because the collection of this sort of information could potentially increase the number of successful convictions in what is a horrendous and often life-altering event for the victim: in the short term, blood transfusions are often required for victims in order to replace lost blood; longer term, severe scarring is not uncommon. On the other hand, if these dustpan and brush kits are used by bar and pub owners, the chain of custody doesn't start with law enforcement personnel — it's an open book for criticism by the defence regarding the manner in which the glass was collected before it reached the hands of the police. A bar manager could choose to 'fit someone up' because, let's face it, the chances are that they know the troublemakers. I think only time will tell with this one but I'd be interested to be involved with cases of this type as an independent expert, just to see how the prosecution laboratories and the police handle the evidence collection side of things.

During my time in England I had the dubious pleasure of being involved with many cases relating to drug traces on banknotes. Unlike those of us living in countries with polymer money, such as New Zealand or Australia, those who live in countries with paper money are carrying around banknotes practically all of which bear minute traces of cocaine. At my last look at the database of English banknotes that had been tested for drug traces, 70 per cent of them bore traces of MDMA (Ecstasy), five per cent bore traces of diamorphine (heroin) and five per cent bore traces of THC (found in cannabis). More than 99 per cent of them bore traces of cocaine. This doesn't necessarily mean that cocaine is the drug most widely used in England and Wales. It just means that, for some reason, traces of cocaine tend to be retained on banknotes more readily than other drugs. The exact mechanism for this is not fully understood but various tests have been undertaken and the banknotes themselves have been examined in various ways, including scanning electron microscopy in order to visualise the structure of banknote surfaces. And the reason analysis of individual banknotes is undertaken? Quite frankly, because they can. I should also add here that it's not just banknotes that are examined. Swabs are also routinely collected from vehicles, mobile phones, clothes and the surfaces of bags containing banknotes. Basically, anything that can be swabbed can and is examined for the presence of drug traces.

Banknotes are seized in a variety of cases including criminal cases, Customs and Excise and under the Proceeds of Crime Act. Before this technology came along, in drug-related cases, particularly dealing and trafficking, large quantities of banknotes were either swabbed en masse or were vacuumed in order to collect any drug traces present. The current method means banknotes can be analysed one by one, which means that if one banknote is very contaminated, it can be picked out.

There are now answers to some previously difficult questions, such as how do you know it wasn't just one heavily contaminated banknote that contaminated all the rest? Or, the outer banknotes were handled by Drug Squad officers so they must have contaminated them and that's what's caused the results. Some nice people at the laboratory will analyse a selection of individual banknotes in a non-destructive manner. Sometimes, those nice people at the laboratory will travel to court to give evidence about what they found. Sometimes, someone like me might go along as well to add comment for the defence. It's been a hard-fought battle to get this method of analysis accepted in court, partly because people like me flogged away at the inadequacies until it reached the stage it's at now. I personally have no problem with the methods, analysis or even the interpretation — as long as it relates only to English sterling banknotes; to my knowledge, there is no adequate database for interpretation of other currencies (except perhaps euros). In my humble opinion, very careful consideration should also be given to databases regarding drug traces in vehicles, on mobile phones and many other items.

In order to be able to understand the sensitivity of the technique that detects tiny drug traces on items like mobile phones, money, clothing and cars, we need to understand the size of the particles that can be detected. The method can detect nanogram weights of drugs. That's 10 to the minus 9 or 0.000000001 gram. To try to understand the size of this, if a single grain of salt were taken and divided into a thousand parts and each of these individual parts were then subdivided again into a thousand parts, one of those final parts would represent the approximate level of sensitivity of the analytical device. Alternatively, if the total amount of drug traces present on one million sterling banknotes (each contaminated at nanograms levels) were bulked together it would amount in size to no more than a single grain of salt. The quantities of drugs potentially detected by this technique are such that the drugs would not be visible with the naked eye.

You have to be careful with this kind of scientific information, though, because it sounds extremely impressive. It's like DNA — once a DNA result has been presented in court, it is extremely hard to cast any measure of doubt on the result, even if it were fundamentally flawed in a given case; it's just a function of the automatic weight that triers of fact place on DNA findings. It's similar with drug traces on items; people are fascinated to hear about the prevalence of these drug traces and it creates an automatic acceptance of the results. In more than one case, though, the defendant's money was found to be contaminated with one drug but he was charged with supply of a different drug altogether. In one case, the problem the police had was that despite a small amount of cannabis found on the defendant at the time of his arrest, there was no bulk quantity of any other drug recovered. He admitted to being a cannabis user but denied supply. The police prosecuted him because high levels of drug traces were found on his money but no one on the Crown's team looked to see that the charge related to cannabis while the money suggested heroin. Who knows where the money came from, but even the police didn't think he was a heroin dealer. The case was chucked out of court. Lesson from this case: take a good look at your whole case, including the scientific results, before bringing charges.

This next story is about drug traces on banknotes and also about court attendance, this time where I was involved as a defence expert for a case in Scotland. I only went because my boss was on holiday somewhere exotic and he couldn't make it, so I had to go. After getting stuck on the M1 on the way to Luton airport (pouring rain, stationary traffic for an hour) I missed my flight to Aberdeen and had to get on the next flight, which was to Edinburgh. Happily, the barrister was in Edinburgh so he picked me up at the airport and we drove to Aberdeen. I have no idea exactly how long it took, except it seemed a very long time in a car with someone I had never met. In fact, I had never even spoken to him before. This is the sort of thing your mother warns you not to do.

I spent four days in Scotland. It snowed and there was no heating in the hotel, even though Rod Stewart was apparently a co-owner. All I can say is that despite being born in England he's truly Scottish with iron for blood and thicker vests than I've ever owned. I had no thermals with me. There was porridge for breakfast, though, which was good, as it meant no other meals were necessary for the rest of the day. It arrived in an enormous bath-sized bowl, three inches deep and accompanied with either salt or nowt. I didn't dare ask for honey in case they muttered about me being a southern Sassenach wuss, and spat in tomorrow's porridge. The Crown's scientists came and went. I stayed, in case I was needed, but I wasn't. The Crown wanted to show the tape of the police interview but no one knew how to work the video player. I know it makes me sound ancient, but DVD players weren't widely used at that time. Rather than allow us to try to work it out for ourselves (three barristers, a solicitor, a judge, three forensic scientists and an assortment of police officers who must have had to deal with videotapes and players on every shift), court was adjourned for half a day so that a technician could drive from Aberdeen to fix it. Only a certified technician was allowed to touch it. The technician duly arrived, pressed a switch, the VCR started to work and we all got back to the trial wondering how life had become so mad and why the technician couldn't have told us over the phone which button to press.

There were many other things about the case that were bizarre including some of the circumstances (the defendant was found guilty; the defendant went to prison; the case was appealed; the defendant was released). I can't really say much more because I'm not sure if there might be some other ongoing issues with it but another odd incident occurred during the original trial. A mobile phone rang (very quietly, I might add). The judge stopped the proceedings and demanded that the offender place at least a pound, but preferably a bank-note of some denomination, into the charity jar he kept on the bench. I leaned over to the solicitor and commented that this was indeed a strange occurrence. He leaned back and said, 'It's just as well we're not in the courtroom next door — the judge in there puts people in the cells for an hour if a phone goes off in his court, even if you're a QC.'

Chapter 11

Pollen
<hr>

Today, I am wondering what happened in my life that meant my working day was reduced to boiling the snot of dead people. Because that is what I am doing. I have eight test tubes, I'm in the laboratory and I'm mentally battling with myself about what the contents of these tubes represent. No matter how I look at it, I can't escape reality: it's snot from dead people. This isn't some kind of punishment inflicted on me because I was naughty or did something wrong. This is part of a research project I dreamed up, along with some colleagues from England, while we were having a beer in the bar during their 2009 visit to give evidence in the Bain retrial. The reason we started to discuss dead people's snot is because we wanted to see if we could come up with a method to collect pollen from the nasal passages of the deceased that was less costly, time consuming and invasive than the previous method.

Pollen analysis is an area of forensic science that doesn't really get the coverage it deserves. That's partly because it seems to have been painted as technically difficult. However, pollen analysis (and I use the term 'pollen' here to include spores as well) is not really any different from other types of trace material. The same factors have to be taken into account when considering collection, sealing of items and examination/processing at the laboratory. The real skill comes in the interpretation because it requires knowledge of botany, ecology, crime scene examination and the forensic arena, in order to be able to make any sense out of it.

When you look out at a meadow or garden in spring time, the sight that meets the eye is of regeneration — new growth, flowers and pretty colours. Floating in among the beautiful posies, billowing grasses and flowering trees are masses of reproduction bodies — pollen and spores. Because not all of those reproduction bodies go on to make new plants, the ones left over are the trace deposits that can be picked up and used by human beings for forensic purposes or for heating our homes. Pollen, spores and microscopic particles made of a compound called sporopollenin, form a component of the fossil fuels we burn in our fireplaces, or in coal-fired power stations. Pollen and spores are also used in the petroleum and gas industries to help find layers of underground rock that might contain those fuels. Of course, those pollen and spores are essentially fossils but the modern ones floating around in the air and settling on surfaces all over the planet are the ones most likely to be encountered in forensic casework, as well as being the ones that cause hay fever. From my academic research perspective, pollen is most commonly used to reconstruct past vegetation communities, which, in turn, tell us about climate and environmental setting at the time the pollen was deposited. For example, I know all about how Auckland's vegetation changed over the last one million years and how it reacted when tonnes of volcanic ash rained down on it from the Auckland and central North Island volcanoes.

It's interesting, it adds fuel to the climate change debate, but it's not often going to solve any crimes. We have to think differently for crime solution.

From the perspective of people who are murdered, their last breath may well contain pollen from the place where they took that last breath. Knowing what plants that pollen represents can sometimes help investigators determine what happened to a person before and/or after they died. Those of a delicate disposition may want to skip this next bit but going back to my cunning plan of boiling dead people's snot, the problem with the previous method of collecting samples from nasal passages was that it was very invasive. It involves removing the top of the skull with a saw, removing the brain (this often occurs during postmortems anyway), peeling off the basal lining of the skull, breaking through the bony base of the skull and into the nasal passages. The corpse is then turned on its side, a warm water and shampoo mixture is flushed through the nasal passages and the emergent liquid is caught in a bowl as it exits the nasal passages. This procedure requires at least two people, one of whom is usually a forensic pollen expert. Because forensic pollen experts aren't routinely present at postmortems, arrangements have to be made for the pathologist, pollen expert and often a police officer to be present — this takes time and costs money because the pollen expert might have to travel from a long way away. The pollen expert also has to bring a whole heap of kit with them to get the job done, just in case the mortuary doesn't have that particular equipment.

Delaying postmortems is not desirable, because not only does it delay the investigation, it also delays the time until the body can be released to the family for the funeral. On a personal note, I would also prefer that if a pollen sample had to be collected from a body that the minimum amount of destruction be done to that body.

Another reason why I thought long and hard about how to collect pollen samples from noses without having to remove brains was purely selfish: I don't want to attend any more postmortems than absolutely essential. A postmortem is a fascinating experience and I've always been totally absorbed with how the body functions. One problem, though, is that I have a very sensitive sense of smell and mortuaries and dead bodies usually have strong smells associated with them. The other thing is that I'm not keen on seeing skin being cut.

I know this because the first postmortem I ever attended resulted in me going very grey as the blood drained from my face, down through my torso and into my legs where it was quite happy to stay. The only thing that had happened at that stage was the pathologist leaning towards the deceased's eyes and pulling them back with tweezers to see if the blood vessels were burst — a classic confirmation that the chap had died as a result of hanging (probably a pretty good clue was the weird angle of his neck). Although my brain really wanted me to look because it was interesting, my basic consciousness decided it was a very bad idea and just shut down, which led to the buckling legs and the smirks from the mortuary assistants who'd been watching me very carefully to see how I'd react. I guess one of them lost the bet about whether or not I'd keel over. After that, the skin was cut and ribs of the deceased were cracked with a special tool. Luckily for me, I was being assisted to a stool while that bit happened.

After I'd recovered, though, the rest of the postmortem was

just amazing. The brain really looked like brains do in books, which might sound silly but it's the same as seeing Big Ben or a real kiwi for the first time — they really do look like they look in the pictures. The kidney cross-section was intricate; the intestines were just all over the place like unstrung sausages. I came away from that postmortem fascinated, educated and horrified in equal measure. And embarrassed, because the pathologist was the same one who did the postmortems on Princess Diana and Dodi Al Fayed. He was very gracious about my temporary staggering and never mentioned it again. He must see that sort of reaction all the time.

So here I am today, boiling snot from dead people to see whether our new, non-invasive technique recovers as much pollen as the old brain-removing approach. I'm happy to say that it does, which, if people use it, means less time wasted at postmortems, less cost and, for me, less chance of having to go to postmortems at three in the morning.

As far as casework goes, those involving pollen don't fall in to any dominant case category, mostly because pollen is such a versatile trace material and because it's present everywhere including, as we have seen, up people's noses. It's not like cases involving glass fragments that, in my casework experience, most often relate to burglaries, break-ins or car theft. Cases involving drug traces usually relate to drugs. Cases involving blood spatter relate to some sort of crime against the person (or, occasionally, against an animal). Pollen as an evidence type occurs across a wide range of cases.

One of the interesting applications of pollen is determining the geographical location in which drug plants were growing when they were harvested, such as *Cannabis sativa* (cannabis plant), *Papaver somniferum* (opium poppy used for making heroin) and *Erythroxylum coca* and other species of *Erythroxylum* (used for preparing cocaine). I also assume this could apply to *Ephedra*, which can be one of the source materials used in the manufacture of methamphetamine, or as it's more commonly called in New Zealand, Pure or P. This would be a good research topic if anyone feels like giving us some funding for it. We've undertaken pollen analysis of drugs for intelligence purposes and had good results but I can't tell you any more about it because it's probably classified information.

A similar use of pollen analysis is to determine whether different batches of cannabis flowering head material grew in separate growing seasons or just one growing season. Both of these types of cases involve washing the pollen grains out of or off the main drug material and examining what other pollen grains are present. Because plants have ecological niches, we use the pollen to paint a virtual picture of the environment in which the plants grew. In the case of cocaine and heroin, it can also be possible to use the pollen content to identify not only where the original plants were grown but also where in the world the pure form of the drug was diluted, or 'cut'.

Other examples of pollen casework are for confirming or refuting alibis. One case involved a defendant who said he had not assaulted a woman in a specific location in a park, although he accepted he had walked through another part of the park. Pollen recovered from her clothing and his shoes showed they had been in the same area of the park as the complainant had indicated; the pollen therefore was not consistent with the defendant's account of events. The reason pollen works in those kinds of cases is because the proportions of different pollen types vary rapidly over relatively short distances, in the order of metres. It means that a 'pollen signature' in the middle of a park will be different from the pollen signature around the edges, or the pollen signature in the middle of your garden will be different from that at the edge of the garden. It therefore stands to reason that the pollen signature at a murder scene in an urban street will be wildly different from the pollen signature in Auckland's Waitakere Ranges, where the body may be dumped.

Other uses of pollen might be to help determine where a person died or what happened to them after they died. I had a case once where a woman's body was found, intact, in a suitcase by the edge of a tidal river. The puzzling thing was that her clothing and, in particular, her hair, had pollen on them that didn't match any of the locations of interest in the case. It was a while before I realised that no one had taken a sample of the river water to see what had been in it; it was perfectly possible that the unexplained pollen had been carried in the river water and deposited on her as the tide washed over the suitcase and soaked into the contents.

In war crimes investigations, pollen has been used to determine whether or not bodies in mass graves were killed elsewhere and transported to the grave. This had serious implications in the late 1990s, during the extended periods of unrest in Central Europe. Mass graves used to bury victims of genocide were dug up again by the perpetrators. The bodies were removed and reburied in other locations, with fewer bodies in each grave. By doing this, the perpetrators said those people had not been the victims of genocide, but had been killed in much smaller confrontations — it's more plausible to explain four people being 'accidentally' shot in crossfire than 50. War crimes investigators then exhumed the smaller graves and took soil samples from the clothes of the victims. In one case, the soil and pollen tied the exhumed bodies with a mass grave in a different location, which, in turn, provided support for claims of genocide.

The solution of a very high profile double murder case in the United Kingdom in 2002, that of Holly Wells and Jessica Chapman, was assisted by pollen analysis. The two 10-year-old schoolgirls went missing in August, during the English summer. After a highly publicised missing person's search, their bodies were eventually discovered near the edge of a Royal Air Force base in the county of Suffolk, eastern England. Pollen analysis of debris from the perpetrator's car helped link him with the site where the girls' bodies were found. The girls had been killed by their school caretaker and his girlfriend helped by providing him with a false alibi, although she was not found to have had any contemporaneous knowledge of him committing the crimes. He received life imprisonment with a minimum of 40 years to be served. She was sentenced to three and a half years for perverting the course of justice, served a total of 21 months and in 2004 was released on probation.

For forensic pollen work, pollen experts might be limited to sediment scraped from the knee of a pair of trousers or perhaps pollen collected from the heads of cannabis plants, but any sort of sediment can be examined for pollen. The thing with pollen cases (with the exception of drugs) is that the casework can involve crimes against the person, which are sometimes the most difficult to work just because of the distress element. However, it's not all about death and addiction.

I spent a very pleasant day at a house in West Auckland once, collecting pollen samples and assisting with the collection of concrete samples and sections of wood from the roof rafters. The owner of the house wanted to stop it being bulldozed during construction of a motorway extension. The only way that could happen was if it could be shown that the house pre-dated the early 1900s — if it did, then it would be protected from demolition by virtue of its age. Both concrete composition and vegetation have changed with time, so by examining samples of both (concrete from the walls, pollen from directly beneath the house) it was possible to provide an indication of when the house was built. Tree ring data also helped determine the ages of the trees that had been felled and used to build the rafters. It was a lovely sunny day when we were out there and the house was in a pleasant little spot. Unfortunately, our combined results indicated that the house was not as old as it needed to be and it disappeared under the bitumen. On this occasion, there may not have been any death and addiction, but there was destruction.

Having demonstrated, albeit briefly, the usefulness of pollen in a forensic setting, it's heartening to know that in the world of academic research, pollen analysis of mammoth dung has been able to help in determining the extinction mechanism of mammoths and other large mammals during the last Ice Age, which ended approximately 10,000 years ago, depending on one's global location. Apparently, a gradual decline in large mammal numbers started around 15,000 years ago and lasted for about 1000 years. This would pretty much rule out a previous suggestion of catastrophic extinction à la the dinosaurs at the Cretaceous-Tertiary boundary of 65 million years ago, as the result of an extraterrestrial object impacting the planet about 13,000 years ago. The study also suggested that mammoths may have had a role to play in the way the vegetation of the time functioned and grew. Scientifically, it's very interesting but from a general perspective I still find it strange that people are surprised that the large mammals are probably more than just a striking addition to an African landscape, but have actually been significant in its development. I'm pretty sure David Attenborough has known that for years.

It's reassuring that analysing excrement can add so much information to our knowledge — an archaeologist I know has spent years analysing coprolites, which are fossilised faecal matter, and preserved (usually desiccated) faeces. By examining coprolites and preserved faeces for the presence of vegetable fibres, pollen, spores, leaf material structures, bones, undigested food, seeds and such like, we can learn a huge amount about an ancient community's diet, general health, eating, foraging and hunting habits. Discussion also abounds about what length of time each coprolite represents — did people have more or less regular bowel movements? Coprolites don't always originate from humans; I know a rock outcrop that contains fish coprolites.

It's fascinating what we can learn from poo. The problem is that although preserved faeces are hard when they're discovered, making them soft enough to study also releases the smell.

Chapter 12

Those 1960s, drug-takin' Fabulous Furry Freak Brothers (and Fat Freddy's Cat)

Amsterdam is well known for its cannabis culture and liberal attitude towards this particular drug. While cultivation of cannabis is still illegal in the Netherlands, sale of the end product is not. As soon as someone in the United Kingdom says they're off for a weekend to Amsterdam, eyebrows go up because everyone knows what they're up to — not necessarily to see the Ladies of the Night but off to get stoned in a coffee shop. It's a popular destination for stag weekends and any other poor excuse for visiting Europe and 'seeing the sights'.

However, it seems the Dutch authorities have had enough of drug tourists flooding the country and causing untold problems. After originally decriminalising consumption and possession of less than five grams of cannabis in 1976, the Dutch government now plans to limit drug tourism by reserving dozens and dozens of the licensed coffee shops for the use of locals only. Some coffee shops are going to become members only clubs, restricting sales to those with a Dutch debit card, which basically removes foreigners from the purchasing pool.

To give you an idea of how many people we're talking

about here, two councils in Holland, which between them have eight such coffee shops, announced they will stop the sale of cannabis in an attempt to stem the weekly flow of 25,000 customers. That's 25,000 drug tourists per week in just two areas. It shows how much of a problem it must be for the Dutch, because that kind of restriction on sale is surely going to have a marked impact on the economy.

Presumably, the change in the Dutch government's stance is due in part to the increased strength of cannabis. This has come about as the result of cross-breeding variants of cannabis plants to increase the THC (delta-9-tetrahydrocannabinol) content. Analysis of cannabis samples over time has shown that Dutch cannabis contained an average of 8.6 per cent THC in 2000, compared with 15.2 per cent in 2002. In my experience, this is not dissimilar to the story in England and Wales and, to my knowledge, it's a similar story here in New Zealand.

Drugs have been a part of life for *Homo sapiens* for thousands of years. There is evidence cannabis was being used in 3000 BC and there is suggestion that Stone Age humans had the under-standing to develop drug paraphernalia. While a definition of how long ago the Stone Age occurred is variable, let's say it was tens of thousands of years ago.

Given the human race's long affiliation with drugs, and for the purposes of this chapter I'm excluding alcohol, it's no surprise that drug cases make up a good part of any independent scientist's casework. Cannabis, which used to occur in New Zealand far more than it does now, has been supplanted by methamphetamine. Rather than needing relatively large areas to cultivate plants plus months to allow for growth, meth can be prepared in a relatively small area in much less time. The profit is greater and, as drugs go, it's far more addictive, meaning that customers are much more likely to come back for more.

Still, cannabis remains a popular drug of production but there are differences in the ways different countries use it. Hash oil, which is reasonably common in New Zealand, isn't something I ever saw in casework in England. It's common enough here that forensic scientists have studied the effect different filtration methods have on the pollen content, bearing in mind that pollen can be used to help determine where the source cannabis plants were grown. Cannabis resin, which is a concentrate of the cannabis plant, is common in the United Kingdom and is mostly imported. It's sprinkled into tobacco a bit like an OXO cube into a stew and is then made into rollies, joints, spliffs — whatever you want to call them. Adding tobacco to spliffs is a very English thing apparently, whereas Kiwis tend to just smoke cannabis flowers on their own and therein lies another difference: leaves and flowers. Sometimes the leaf and flowering head material from cannabis exhibits will be weighed together. As any self-respecting cannabis user will tell you, when using cannabis plant material, the flowering head is what gives the best high.

And as any self-respecting drugs scientist will tell you, that's because the greatest concentration of the active compound of cannabis, THC, is found in the flowering heads of the female plants. Leaf material is smoked in the United Kingdom far more than it is in New Zealand. Kiwis flog off bags of leaf material ('cabbage') to ex-pat Brits who think Christmas has come early because they can score cheap cannabis in New Zealand. They don't know the Kiwis couldn't give it away otherwise. International micro-economies at work.

Although cannabis grows very happily outdoors in New Zealand, there is the problem that someone might accidentally stumble across your plantation or it might be spotted from the air by police reconnaissance missions. An anecdote I heard recently recounts how a woman hanging out her washing on one of the offshore islands glanced up to see what she thought might be the WestPac Rescue Helicopter. Turned out to be a police helicopter from which was dangling a police officer in brightly coloured orange overalls clutching a huge bundle of fully grown cannabis plants to his chest as the wind buffeted him about. More interesting work stories indeed.

The answer to unplanned removal of cannabis plants is to grow it inside or under cover. Whole houses in the United Kingdom are devoted to growing cannabis plants; the growers pay someone to go in and check on the plants, adjust the growing conditions and generally make sure the junk mail isn't piling up on the door mat and drawing suspicion. The advantage for the growers of those set-ups is that no one actually lives at the house so if it's raided by the police only the plants are seized and probably the caretaker; the main players remain one step removed. However, many people just set aside a small area of their premises for smaller scale cultivation.

One such case was where Mr Jones had grown cannabis plants in a special room in his house. He said the cannabis was for his and his mother's personal use, because his mother had cancer and it was the only thing that helped her manage her condition. A relevant point here is that there is at least one prescription drug on the market containing the active ingredient of cannabis. However, patients who have been prescribed this drug reported the unwanted side effects that can result from cannabis use — increased anxiety, paranoia or the occurrence of panic attacks, feeling nauseous, dizzy, clammy and the associated draining of colour from the skin resulting in a condition referred to as a 'whitey'. The patients' main concern was that the capsule form of the drug didn't allow them to minimise the dose they received, which is why research has been under way to develop a nasal spray.

Anyway, Mr Jones' assertion that the cannabis was for his mother's benefit, although not legal, might have some sway with the court on compassionate grounds, coupled with the reported benefits. The police took a different view and were of the opinion that Mr Jones had grown this lovely, juicy crop of green, green cannabis to dry and sell to anyone willing to pay.

Mr Jones said his mother used to smoke cannabis by the traditional cannabis cigarette method. Unfortunately, Mother Jones had to give up smoking so her son started making cups of cannabis tea for her instead.

Part of my job in the case was to determine how many cups of cannabis tea the seized weight of cannabis could have made and whether that number was feasible or not for personal use. When I asked for the cup he used so that I could make a valid estimation, I duly received the most enormous drinking mug I have ever seen. I was expecting a coffee cup, perhaps a large tea mug at best, but this thing was huge. It meant that seven cups of tea per day increased the volume of cannabis used per day from a few grams to tens of grams. This meant the total volume of cannabis seized wouldn't have lasted as long with the bowl-with-handle cup compared with a standard cup; it went to the credibility of the story and whether or not the total mass seized could have reasonably been for personal use, as he was claiming. Small cup meant less likely; large cup meant more likely, assuming the court could be persuaded accordingly.

All seemed well and good for the defendant — I could almost hear his solicitor thinking he could be in with a fighting chance here. Then I asked about how the cannabis tea was made. The order of ingredients and manner in which the drinks were made was crucial to the credibility of the defendant's account. I needed the defendant's description of how he made the tea *before* I said anything else. As it turned out, the way the defendant says he made the tea wouldn't have released the active ingredient from the cannabis material — which meant the tea drinker would have had a nice hot cup of wet cannabis flowers but wouldn't have got stoned.

On the day of the trial, I met with the prosecution expert, which was good as far as I was concerned, because it just so happened he was an extremely experienced scientist who agreed with what I was saying. He was a nice chap, too. We had to sit in a pokey interview room while the trial was in progress and, unusually, we were allowed to sit together — although we were very tactfully reminded not to discuss the case at hand.

We did talk about other drugs, though, and it was *fascinating.* The prosecution scientist was from an era when forensic scientists were trained in all aspects of the art, not like now when they're trained in very narrow fields. He was also part of the laboratory where they actually tested the effects of drugs.

On themselves. Get this — they were paid by the government to take illicit drugs to see what effects they had. They took all sorts — LSD, Ecstasy, cannabis, cocaine, magic mushrooms, heroin, the worm at the bottom of a tequila bottle — you name it, they took it. I can see the logic behind using forensic scientists for testing, because it always strikes me as less than ideal when we're asked about the effects of drugs and all we can talk about are the measured levels in blood samples because we can't speak from experience. Can you imagine that happening now — paying people to get stoned at work? You'd have P-addicted scientists charging round the countryside and munchy-eating cannabis smokers drifting round the lab and falling asleep in the lunch room.

Anyway, back to Mr Jones. He was found guilty of cultivation and supply. Next time, know how to make tea.

Mr Jones' case was unusual, in that I've not encountered another tea-making case. Usually, it's all about how the cannabis was grown and whether sufficient was present at the time of seizure to account for personal use or whether it was enough to constitute supply/dealing. Each jurisdiction has different ways of dealing with the matter and different methods of cultivation are employed. In the United Kingdom, cannabis is generally grown most successfully as part of a hydroponic cultivation. Hydroponic cultivation set-ups are usually relatively sophisticated. They are usually located in a dedicated part of a house or building, the walls are often painted white and/or lined with aluminium cooking foil to reflect the light and heat. They'll have fans, heat lamps and high-intensity lights on timers, to regulate the amount of light and heat available to the plants. They'll have troughs containing nutrient-rich water being circulated by pumps. There might be an area dedicated to propagating seedlings or cuttings taken from a 'mother' plant, which is a plant known to produce good cannabis, so clones are taken from it.

As I mentioned before, cannabis can grow quite happily outdoors in New Zealand, where it behaves like a weed (weed by name, weed by nature). Not generally so in England, so I was caught off-guard when I received an enquiry from a lawyer in England, whose client was claiming that the plant seized by the police from his property was a cucumber plant, in excess of six feet tall. It was growing by the side of a garage in southern England, not far from the A1, and had been spotted by someone with a trained eye driving along. Suffice to say, it wasn't a cucumber plant and it wouldn't have won prizes at the local A&P show. I expect that instead of ending up neatly sliced into dainty sandwiches, this 'cucumber' went the way of all seized drugs — destroyed.

Although production of cannabis has reduced in New Zealand, it's still clearly going strong elsewhere. According to the BBC in 2009, up to £100 million of cannabis is grown in Scotland each year, and is worth more than the entire Scottish vegetable crop. Hydroponic cultivation seems to be pretty much the same everywhere and the use of entire buildings and hijacking the electricity supply for cannabis cultivation are common. I remember a case where a hidden room had been constructed in a house with an entrance through a secret door halfway up the stairs — although obviously not that secret because the police found it in the end but, still, when I saw the photos it was all very Famous Five. Joking aside, though, large-scale cannabis cultivation is a very real problem with very real issues behind it — human trafficking, organised crime.

'Skunk' is a strong, pervasively pungent variety of cannabis and is up to three times stronger than other types of cannabis. The British government recently reclassified cannabis from Class C to B to reflect the fact that skunk is now the dominant form of cannabis being sold on the British market. Some scientists are of the opinion that skunk may have a higher risk of causing mental health problems than other varieties. Skunk in the latter part of the first decade of the twenty-first century accounts for about three-quarters of police cannabis seizures; in 2003 the figure was much lower, at just 15 per cent. That's a massive increase, and just goes to show the skill cannabis growers have developed in hybridisation.

Aside from cannabis, New Zealand's other traditional drugs of abuse include P and heroin. Although the use of heroin isn't unusual globally, Kiwis used their famous number eight mentality and came up with a way of making heroin at home so they didn't have to bother with pesky imports at high risk of being intercepted by customs. This new home-cooking method, known not surprisingly as home-bake, started to pick up pace in the early 1980s when there was a sharp decline in the amount of heroin making it onshore.

Although heroin use continues here at a lower level, New Zealand's P problem, on the other hand, is now a significant industry. The manufacturing process mostly uses household items and commonly available chemicals. The use of P has increased dramatically over the past eight years; when I went back to England in 2002 it hadn't really registered on the radar but by the time I got back in 2008, there were barely enough police and ESR experts to keep up with the casework demand, and both organisations now have teams specialising in P lab investigation. In much the same way as I would navigate around England using pubs as landmarks, a colleague marks his way around Auckland based on the P labs he's investigated — not a suburb is clear of them. New Zealand has world-class expertise in identification of P labs, clan lab clean up, yield calculations and property remediation/ air quality testing. It's a marketable skill the rest of the world is needing to learn from us. Sad but true. By the way, a 'clan lab' is the usual term these days used to refer to a clandestine or illegal laboratory, and has recently started making its way into the media and more common usage.

One of the problems with P labs is that even after they've been busted or dismantled, the drug itself lingers in the property. Painting or wallpapering over surfaces doesn't get rid of the problem because it just seeps through to the surface again. Full replacement of gib board or total demolition of the property are sometimes the only remedies. My serious advice when buying a house would be to make sure you have the air quality tested for the presence of methamphetamine residues *before* signing on the dotted line.

Because the application of forensic science usually takes place at the instigation of the police/Crown/prosecution, the types of science applied to casework are dictated by the capabilities and laboratory equipment available in each laboratory or organisation. This means that not all forensic science laboratories are created equal. Take drugs cases, for example — there are a number of different methods available for examining drugs but they're not all used in all laboratories. A reasonable proportion of drugs cases I reviewed in England and Wales involved looking at the wrappings that contained the drugs. Makes sense really, when you consider that all drugs are wrapped in something or other.

Blister packs

Prescription drugs often arrive in these things. It's a terrible albeit descriptive name. I can't help imagining tablets erupting from the packaging in small floods of semi-transparent fluid, just like back in the days of popping blisters after finishing cross-country runs through the pouring rain at school. Contac NT, the starter product for making P, is produced in blister packs. Unless it is stolen or otherwise acquired before being packaged into blister packs, someone cracks the capsules out of the packaging, one at a time. Each capsule contains hundreds of tiny balls of medication about a millimetre in diameter. In case you're wondering, the same people don't then usually spend their time pulling the little capsules apart and emptying the balls into a bucket; they often just stick the capsules in a blender or a coffee grinder and flick on the power.

Kitchen foil

Some drugs, like 'crack' cocaine, occur in lumps, known as rocks, and are often wrapped in small parcels of kitchen foil. Kitchen foil tears nicely and the ends of torn pieces can be matched together to see if smaller pieces originated from a larger piece or if they were ripped off a roll found in someone's kitchen. Putting the pieces back together again is called a *physical fit* and it's a bit like putting together a jigsaw.

Cling film or food wrap

I visited a food wrap and poly bag factory once. I know it sounds like a bad school day-trip, but it was very entertaining. I saw barrels of tiny polymer pellets being melted down in giant vats, like something out of *Charlie and the Chocolate Factory*, and then blown though a circular mould called a 'die', which makes an enormous long bubble of transparent polymer. The bubble is then cut to different lengths and rolled onto tubes to make food wrap or cut, folded and heat-sealed to make grip or zip lock bags. Knowing about the manufacturing process means we can consider colour, construction, size, optical properties, surface damage and chemical analysis of the polymer that forms the basis of the bag or food wrap. I haven't seen bag or food wrap comparison used very often in New Zealand, but it is a valid and very useful technique.

Along with alcohol, I find drug cases are among the most interesting, which I guess is a good thing professionally because it doesn't look like either is in decline.

Chapter 13

Walk along the imaginary line until I tell you to stop

A policewoman once got very huffy with me because I demonstrated some of the English police's impairment tests during a presentation I gave in New Zealand. She said that I'd given the game away and now people would know what to expect when the police stopped them and I'd ruined it *all*. Firstly, people cannot control how they react to drugs so regardless of whether or not you know that you're going to be doing a one-leg stand or walking an imaginary line, if you're stoned off your trolley, you won't be able to do it properly. Secondly, the self-same tests have been shown in many real-life follow-the-police-around TV programmes, so they're no secret. Thirdly, the people I was addressing were business ladies of a certain age group, many of whom had never heard of some of the things I was talking about. I know you can't judge a book by its cover but I think it was unlikely they were the sorts of women who would be going into the toilets to snort a line of coke off the cistern with their platinum cards and then avoid doing a roadside impairment test on the way home. Although you never can tell.

Toxicology is the study of the fate of substances once they

enter the body, by whatever means — maybe the person ate them, drank them, absorbed them through their skin, breathed them in or injected them. Forensic toxicology is traditionally considered in relation to drugs but toxicology in its own right relates to many other compounds and could include anything from pesticides to gas inhalation or injection of heroin. The father of a colleague recently had a heart attack, caused by the absorption of a garden insecticide through his skin when he sprayed it on his hand. In that case, a hospital toxicologist would have been involved in determining the levels of chemicals in the patient's body. In theory, anything could be toxic; it's a question of dose and species.

A forensic toxicologist needs to know how a drug breaks down when it enters the body and how to detect those break-down products (metabolites). The kinds of samples forensic toxicologists receive in the laboratory are not the sort that most people would want to handle just before lunch time: blood, urine, stools or body parts such as a livers or liquid from the eyeball. Toxicology is a vastly complicated world, dealing with the inner workings of the human body, and it takes a special set of skills to interpret toxicology results.

Toxicology crops up most commonly (in my experience anyway) in rape and sexual assault cases, murders, drug driving and prison urine screening tests, because no drugs are allowed in prison and the Powers That Be do check. One of the most familiar kinds of case involving toxicology is the date rape drug case, also referred to as Drug Facilitated Sexual Assault (DFSA).

Whether or not date-rape drink spiking is a real problem is a debate I have been following for some years. An article in the *Daily Mail* at the latter end of 2009, which contained comment by a well-respected forensic toxicologist based at the London laboratory of the Forensic Science Service, suggested that DFSA is a minor problem which is far outweighed by the problem of heavy alcohol consumption. My casework experience bears this out. It is sad to say that I have been involved as a forensic science consultant on many rape cases in the past and pretty much all of them involved excessive alcohol consumption on the part of both parties. There was a single memorable case where an allegation of rape was made that didn't involve alcohol. However, the 'evidence' of the assault had been falsified. In particular, the complainant said her jeans had been torn off her as she lay on a bed. Our experiments and research showed it was impossible for the jeans to have been torn in the way suggested. In fact, microscopic examination of the buttonholes showed that at least part of them had been cut.

As a woman, I am sometimes expected to champion the cause of women's rights and the problems of female oppression. Unfortunately, on the date-rape drug debate I cannot fight the corner and don't feel that I should be expected to do so. Rape is a very real problem and everything possible should be done to deal with the issue and prevent it, where possible. However, excess alcohol consumption has skyrocketed in recent years, particularly among women. This to me represents the far greater risk. Excessive alcohol consumption will lead to varying degrees of incapacitation, even in someone who considers they can take their drink. To my mind, the closing line of the *Daily Mail* article says it all: *whatever the risks of the drink spiker coming after you — the chances are that alcohol will get to you first.*

There are a number of drugs that could, theoretically, be used as a 'date-rape' drug, the most common ones being those that induce sleep or stupefaction. All of the date-rape drugs (just like any other drug) have a residence time in the body, which varies. This is one of the key issues when considering the results of a blood sample analysis and it's where the skills of the forensic toxicologist come to the fore. Date-rape drugs (and others) can also be detected in hair. Of the cases where I have suggested hair samples be analysed, no date-rape drugs have been detected, with one exception. GHB (also known as gamma-hydroxybutyric acid or gammahydroxybutyrate) usually pops up, but that's because the body naturally manufactures the substance and its presence is to be expected in hair strand samples. It is therefore the variation in concentration that is important.

I'm not saying that drug-facilitated sexual assault doesn't occur, because it certainly does. I'm also not saying that there's little point in testing for drugs in hair samples because hair sample testing is one of those things that can't be faked, unlike urine, for which there is a thriving black market in 'clean' samples. Hair sample analysis can also be critical to demonstrate the drug use history of someone who wants access to their children, but has been denied because of a previous drug abuse problem.

What I *am* saying is that a lot of people suffer at the hands of excess alcohol consumption.

Drug driving is a peculiar offence, not because it's uncommon, because it's not. An enormous number of people take all kinds of drugs and then drive because they think they're OK, particularly with prescription drugs that may or may not be mixed with other drugs and alcohol. Drug driving is peculiar because it was traditionally a difficult area in which to achieve successful prosecution. It's not like drink driving, where there are legal limits written in to the law that, if exceeded, generally mean guilt of a specific offence. Alcohol is poured into the body and, once absorbed, is eliminated at a relatively constant rate; people behave in a reasonably predictable manner at given blood alcohol concentrations.

Drugs are a different kettle of fish altogether, because there can be significant variation in effects between different individuals, as a result of factors such as individual tolerance and history of drug use or habituation. The effects caused by a combination of drugs, including alcohol, can be exceedingly complex and cannot be predicted with any degree of certainty. Toxic effects depend on the degree of tolerance acquired by the individual concerned. This all sounds like what so many reporters tell me is a scientific cop-out, but it's true – we just can't say what will definitely happen when someone mixes drugs.

Drug driving is illegal in many countries, including New Zealand and the United Kingdom. New Zealand changed the law to try to increase the rate of successful prosecutions. These changes, which came into force in December 2009, included giving the police the power to conduct roadside impairment tests, similar to those introduced five years earlier in England and Wales. As a forensic scientist working largely for the defence at that time, these changes resulted in more casework coming through the door and more successful prosecutions.

As long as the police covered off all relevant points it was very unlikely a case would fail. My job was to assess whether or not the various points had been covered. These included:

- A witness (including a police officer) who could talk about the manner of driving at the time in question. Driving very slowly down the motorway usually attracts the attention of the police and might suggest the driver is under the influence of a depressant of some sort. Conversely, charging along the outside lane of the motorway at one-and-a-half times the speed limit will probably also attract someone's attention.

- The results of roadside impairment tests undertaken by the driver under the supervision and direction of a specially trained police officer. If the officer deemed that the driver had performed poorly then there were grounds for arrest and transfer of the driver to the police station. This is the subjective part of the procedure and is a function not only of how well the officer has absorbed the training but also how many impairment tests they've conducted and how many stoned people they've seen. A recent weekend police drink- and drug-driving operation in West Auckland involved stopping over 9000 vehicles. How many drug-impaired drivers were detected? None.

- Once at the police station, a medic was required to examine the driver. This allowed the medic to rule out any medical cause for the impairment observed by the police officer at the scene — the driver usually had to redo some or all of the impairment tests. If the medic formed the opinion that the driver was impaired through the use of drugs, a blood sample could be taken. Without this opinion, the taking of a blood sample was not allowed. I saw more than one case where the original reason for stopping the driver wasn't good enough in the eyes of the court and the driver hadn't exhibited many signs of impairment by the time the medic arrived, usually due to a two-hour delay because it was a Saturday night. In those circumstances, there was a chance the blood sample would be ruled inadmissible and the case would fall apart.

- The blood sample would be analysed to detect the presence of a range of commonly encountered drugs, both prescription and illegal, which can adversely affect driving performance. Some drug or metabolite would need to be identified in order to confirm that the driver may have been under the influence of drugs at the time in question. The blood sample result was not sufficient on its own. Finding metabolites of cannabis weren't good enough either, because they don't make a person high and they can also remain in the body for days or even weeks after the effects of cannabis have passed.

All of the above have to be in place for a successful prosecution. The law change in New Zealand seems to be along similar lines but only time will tell how well the police and the legal system deal with the changes.

Despite the law changes in England and Wales appearing to

be successful, in 2009 the government in the United Kingdom announced a new ad campaign warning of the dangers of drug driving. The adverts were to advise drivers that the police can spot the signs of whether someone may be under the influence of drugs using the tag line, *Your eyes will give you away.*

It's true, of course. People cannot control how drugs affect them, particularly when combined, such as cocaine and alcohol. Depressants such as cannabis impair a driver's perception of distance, time and speed as well as restrict the ability to do two things at once, such as look for traffic and change gear. Cocaine is a stimulant and can cause people to take risks, such as driving at high speed in a dangerous manner. Both can have lethal consequences in today's traffic conditions.

I have given evidence in drug-driving cases on several occasions, most notably once in an appeal against conviction. The medic described the impairment tests, including a practical demonstration. The triers of fact (the judge and two magistrates) immediately called an adjournment, which suggests to me they were out the back trying the impairment tests to see how easy or hard they were. I can tell you that they're not something you want to try wearing high heels and a tight skirt.

Chapter 14

Smelly shoes and stinky socks

Who'd want a job where you have to stick your hand in the smelly shoes of people you don't know? Who'd have a job where you have to put your own feet into the same shoes? Forensic footwear examiners, that's who. At least we wear gloves and put plastic bags on our feet before we do either of those things, but you can't escape the smell from a pair of shoes that have been in a bag for a year since they were spattered with bodily fluids of varying colours and consistencies; no amount of biohazard labels stops the stench.

Footwear marks are not to be confused with footprints. Footprints are the marks deposited when someone's bare, or partially bare, foot has contact with a depositional surface. Footprints are the feet equivalent of fingerprints; they are made of skin, are unique to individual people, develop in the womb just like fingerprints and are treated in the same way as fingerprints in the way they are collected from crime scenes, off objects and from suspects. Footprints are relatively uncommon, whereas fingerprints are one of the most common methods of identifying 'persons of interest'.

Footwear marks or impressions, on the other hand, pop up in casework all the time, particularly in burglaries. They are also a sad legacy of serious assaults involving someone being on the receiving end of, literally, a good kicking.

So how do footwear cases work? Easy. Pattern matching. Footwear, such as shoes, boots, jandals/flip flops (depending on where you live), stilettos or whatever people wear on their feet, all have patterns on the soles. Soles leave patterns on surfaces. Match the pattern on a surface with the sole of a shoe — tie a suspect to a crime scene. In theory, it's simple. So how many cases have conclusive matches between the shoes seized from a suspect and patterns recovered from a crime scene? Well, that's something else entirely.

Obtaining a decent footwear mark from a crime scene is partly luck at the time the mark was deposited, partly skill on behalf of the crime scene examiner. Paper is pretty good for recording marks, so if you identify a possible entry point in your house (such as a loose window latch), put nice, clean white paper on the surfaces under the window so that if an intruder does get in, they'll land on the paper and leave a nice mark or two. Try to ensure the paper is on a firm surface — carpet is soft and the mark might distort. Kitchen lino can be pretty good for recording marks but you might not be able to see them with the naked eye, in which case the crime scene people will come along and enhance the marks with special techniques designed to maximise the detail.

Deep shag pile carpet is generally terrible for recording marks — too much flexibility and movement in the fibres. Best case scenario from long pile carpet is usually a vague indication of the size of the footwear mark, perhaps some idea of sole pattern, but not much else.

Footwear marks and impressions made in soil or mud

normally contain less fine detail than marks left on paper. Impressed marks, on the other hand, such as those made on a soft surface like damp mud, may record information about the depth of tread on a shoe, which is the sort of detail that can't usually be determined from a footwear mark on a flat, unyielding surface.

Footwear impressions in soil or similar material can be 'cast' using plaster of Paris or something similar, just as dentists do when taking an impression of someone's teeth. The soil off the casts can be used for all sorts of useful purposes, such as pollen, soil and mineral analysis.

There are of course several factors to take into account when trying to interpret footwear marks recovered from crime scenes and comparing them with shoes from a suspect. When shoes are new or unworn the sole patterns are usually the same on all the shoes that were produced using the same mould. Shoes with the same sole patterns share what is termed the same 'class characteristics' — they're not unique or individual so you'd be hard pressed to distinguish one set of brand new shoes from another, except if there's a little air bubble caught when molten material is poured into the mould.

I have seen several cases where air bubbles were visible on the sole of a shoe and in a mark from a crime scene. When combined with other information about the pattern on the shoe's sole, it has resulted in a conclusive link between a shoe and a crime scene mark.

When items of footwear are used, the soles become worn and after even a short period of time may exhibit various cuts and other damage features which are likely to be unique to that particular item. These are termed 'individualising characteristics' and can be used to conclusively link a shoe with a particular crime scene mark. Think of when you buy a nice new pair of shoes and after your first walk down the street, the soles are scratched, whether you're wearing Nike Air Max or Manolo Blahnik. I think drawing pins have gone out of fashion these days, because when I was at school, people always had drawing pins stuck in their shoes — that'd make for interesting crime scene marks.

Sometimes, of course, on the basis of general pattern, a shoe can be *excluded* from having made a particular mark — a sole with a triangle block pattern isn't going to leave behind patterns of squares and circles. In general terms, the attributes normally compared in footwear mark comparisons usually include the following.

- The moulded sole pattern. This is classified on the basis of the elements that make up a sole pattern, such as bars, blocks, wavy ridges.
- The size of the shoe that made the crime mark. This only works where the entire sole can be seen. In cases where marks are not representative of the whole sole, for example, a bit's missing because the wearer trod partly on the nice piece of white paper but partly on the carpet, things get a bit trickier. This isn't helped by the fact that some manufacturers use the same mould for shoes of different (albeit similar) size.
- The degree of wear present. In some cases, a transient pattern results from frictional forces causing abrasion as the wearer scuffs or drags the sole as part of their day-to-day activity. Although the pattern changes rapidly,

it can be used to conclusively link a footwear item with a crime scene mark. This usually only happens when the shoes are seized by the police really soon after the crime, or if the shoes haven't been worn or worn very little since the time of the crime. This sometimes happens in serious crimes such as assault or murder, where the perpetrator doesn't want to risk ditching the shoes so they hide them somewhere. There was a murder case in the USA once where a pair of shoes worn at the time of the murder was thrown over the side of a bridge in winter. Instead of landing safely in the water, they became stuck on a ledge where they were found weeks and weeks later, perfectly serviceable from a forensic science examination point of view.

• The presence or absence of the individualising characteristics I mentioned earlier, bearing in mind that if there's a time delay between a mark being made and recovery of footwear, the shoes may have acquired additional damage features and ones that were present at the time of the incident could have been obliterated.

Part of what I do as an independent expert in footwear cases is review the work completed by the prosecution expert. Although I made it sound nice and easy, an eye for detail, particularly at the magnified or microscopic level, is crucial. You have to 'get your eye in', as my grandpa would say. It's like looking at one of those 3-D pictures that were popular in the 1990s, where you have to go cross-eyed to see the picture but when you do, it all becomes clear. Examining footwear marks can be like that; one minute it's all just a mass of smears and bits of pattern, the next it's slipped quietly into place and you feel pretty pleased with yourself.

Having decent (as in cool) shoes among your peer group has been pretty important for a long time; think back to the days of teddy boys and brothel creepers, winkle-pickers, pixie boots, Doc Martens, Converse All Stars, the list goes on. One of the things that makes footwear mark examination successful is the enormous range of trainers that have flooded the market. In the 1990s manufacturers saw an opportunity and started making lots of variations on a theme, some of which cost a small fortune. It was pretty handy because it meant lots of different shoes were made with different designs and, most importantly, different sole patterns. It helped that they were comfy to wear and had good grip, which came in handy for shimmying up walls and hopping fences.

Having the latest pair of Nikes used to be crucial to street cred and burglars tend to be young men to whom having cool shoes is important — put the two together and you have a sub-population up to no good wearing reasonably distinctive footwear. Work has recently been completed at the University of Leicester, England, which indicates Reebok Classic trainers were the most popular style of training shoe worn by burglars in the county of Nottinghamshire, which ties in very nicely with my knowledge of English burglaries. The research also found that burglars from poorer areas tended to wear more expensive shoes; burglars with a job had less expensive trainers than those who were unemployed. This leads me to wonder whether employed burglars did it for fun or to supplement their incomes? Did the unemployed burglars have an average income greater than the employed burglars because they received more government benefits? Understandably perhaps, the study had no knowledge of whether said trainers had been stolen or bought legitimately.

A recent paper in the international science publication, *Nature,* could put a spanner in the works if anyone decided mass marketing of training or running shoes was bad for the general population. The paper discussed the issue of human beings running barefoot for thousands of years compared with the relatively recent advent and widespread use of modern running shoes.

The paper described how long-distance runners who usually run barefoot most often land on the fore-feet/ball area before bringing down their heel. By way of contrast, those who wear running shoes mostly land heel first because the shoe provides cushioning and slight elevation. Study of running technique showed that barefoot runners who landed on their ball region generated smaller collision forces when they landed on the ground than those wearing running shoes. The net conclusion was that the foot-landing technique used by barefoot runners could protect feet and lower limbs from some of the impact-related injuries from which many runners now suffer.

It's an interesting paper and probably no surprise. However, in forensic science we have come to rely on the massive variation in, and constantly changing patterns on, the soles of trainers/running shoes. These patterns have been immensely useful for identifying particular pairs of shoes connected with crime. Even narrowing it down to a particular brand and model can help. If there were fewer patterns because there were fewer trainers (resulting in greater numbers of shoes with the same sole pattern), burglary cases would be much more difficult to solve, particularly Johnny Recidivist, doing 10 burglaries over a weekend. There's a counter-side to everything, isn't there?

One of the first crime scenes I ever attended was a fire in South Auckland. As is often the case, it didn't stay as just a fire-related case; for me the most interesting aspect was the footwear mark. By the time we reached the house, some of the windows had been boarded up but everything was pretty much as it had been shortly after the fire. The owner said someone had broken into his house, set a fire in the sitting room and then left the same way they'd come in. The insurance company was having none of it and said the owner had set the fire himself.

One of the first things we did was check for signs of forced entry; if there were any then it would add credibility to the owner's account of events, if there weren't then it was inconclusive at best or, in the eyes of the insurance company, support for the contention that the fire had been facilitated by the owner. We could see nothing untoward around any of the windows or most of the doors of the house.

However, when we looked at the back door, it was a different story. The back door was a simple, two-layer, hollow board construction with two hinges at one side and a handle and opening/locking mechanism in the usual location about halfway up the door. To the side of the handle and lock was what would be expected — a thumping great footwear mark from the sole of a fire officer's standard-issue boot. This was where entry had been forced by the fire service and was in accordance with the fire investigation report.

Just to the side and slightly below that very dominant mark

were two or three faint sole marks from some other type of footwear. The shapes and movement in the marks (that is, they looked scuffed and out of focus) were consistent with them having been made when the door had been *in situ* and prior to the fire officer kicking in the door. Although we couldn't put an age on the marks, it was something of interest and this case was really the first that sparked my interest in forensic science. Unfortunately for the house owner, the insurance company didn't find in his favour and they didn't pay out.

Luckily for me, my first experiences of fire cases were more encouraging than those of a colleague. He attended a fatal house fire and wandered nervously into the scene, trying to look as if he knew what he was doing. Fire scenes are littered with debris and it takes a while to see what you're supposed to be seeing. He found a fire officer in what had been the sitting room and asked him, in as professional a manner as he could summon, where he could find the body. The reply was 'You're standing on him.' The poor victim had literally burnt to a crisp and was but a mere smear and collection of bone fragments, cloth and charcoal on the floor.

Unfortunately, footwear marks are not just found on floors or other inanimate surfaces; occasionally they turn up on people. There was a case once where a chap was found dead in a park in the early hours of an autumn morning. Shoes were seized from two suspects who'd been seen in the company of the deceased earlier the previous day. As is often the case, large quantities of alcohol had been consumed by all involved, so who knows what state of mind everyone was in when it all kicked off, as it were.

Photographs were taken of injuries on the head of the deceased and these were compared with the sole patterns and the uppers of the shoes seized from the two co-defendants. The first defendant, for whom I was undertaking the review, said that although he was with the deceased and the co-defendant on the evening of the incident, he didn't strike any blows to the deceased.

As the independent expert, I was asked to consider the findings of the prosecution expert and whether the bruises on the victim's head could have been caused by either of the pairs of shoes seized.

When an item is used to inflict an injury on an individual, a contusion or bruise may result, or sometimes the skin is broken. Comparison of bruising patterns can be used to draw conclusions regarding whether a given item may have caused a certain bruise. In some cases, it's possible to identify characteristic features to connect a specific item of footwear with a specific bruise. Conversely, in many cases, the bruising is simply not clear enough for any comment to be made regarding the item that caused the bruising.

In this particular case, one pair of trainers had a sole with a sort of yin-yang pattern and the uppers were quite unusual — I'd never seen anything like them before and neither had the prosecution expert. The thing with cases like this is you then spend the next two weeks looking at people's shoes to see if you can spot another pair, but I've never seen one; maybe it's because all three people involved were from Eastern Europe and they'd been shoe shopping at home and brought back something interesting.

The second pair of trainers had a simple sole pattern of rhomboids and the structure of the uppers was completely different from the first pair.

As a result of my examination, I determined that the bruises on the head of the deceased could have been made by footwear attributed to the first defendant but the problem was that the laboratory database wasn't big enough to draw any real conclusions. Of significance in this case was the fact that the footwear had never been seen before by either the prosecution expert or me and the first defendant had already accepted that he'd been with the deceased and the co-defendant on the night in question. It came down to the likelihood of the marks being caused to the head of the deceased by either the first co-defendant or by someone else wearing similar shoes who happened to come along that same evening and kick the victim to death.

It was far more likely to have been the first defendant rather than someone at random so it came down to the fact that the first defendant said that even if he had been present while the deceased was on the ground, he might only have knocked his head with his foot by mistake and if he did knock his head by mistake, he only did it once.

This defence is kind of like the naughty schoolboy approach, of which a colleague of mine is particularly fond, which says, *I wasn't there when the window was broken but if I was then I didn't do it but if I did do it then it was an accident.* I guess it's about covering all bases.

I think what you should do now is go and look at the soles of some shoes.

Sock prints in casework are somewhat unusual because sock prints are usually just a general outline of the foot that made them. If people are in someone else's house when they shouldn't be, they're usually wearing some sort of footwear. The most memorable sock-print cases for me have involved people being in a property when they have been invited or when they lived there. In normal circumstances, finding the sock prints of someone who lives in a given house isn't something likely to be of great interest. When it does get interesting is when the socks have something on them that makes them a little unusual, such as blood.

The two most interesting cases I can describe both relate to murders and both relate to bloodied sock prints deposited on floors.

The circumstances of the first case were that a woman and her boyfriend had her boyfriend's friend staying in their home with them. They had all been out drinking and when they came home, the woman ended up dead on the kitchen floor, stabbed with a kitchen knife. The boyfriend (let's call him Mr Boyfriend) and his mate (we can call him Mr Mate) were both charged with murder and each blamed the other for the woman's death. Mr Mate said that Mr Boyfriend and his girlfriend had gone back to the house on their own and when he arrived at the house the woman was already dead.

The interesting thing at the crime scene was that the woman was dead on the kitchen floor and two sets of bloodied sock prints could be seen tracking through the house. One set was fairly average in size and the other was markedly larger. Mr Mate said that the marks couldn't have been made by him and they therefore must have been made by the deceased and her boyfriend. That was relatively easy to sort out because the deceased had small feet and even allowing for the fact that her test foot impressions had been made by rolling ink onto her feet and pressing her inked feet onto paper while she was lying on her back in the mortuary, her feet couldn't have made either sets of sock prints. So who did leave them?

Each of the defendants was asked to make test impressions, which involved them wearing socks, walking onto ink and then walking down a long sheet of paper. One set of prints in the house matched the size, emplacement and gait of Mr Boyfriend. The other set matched Mr Mate. Mr Mate strongly denied any involvement but unfortunately for him, he had a peculiar arrangement of toes and foot outline. We knew this because a forensic podiatrist had taken a look at the test impressions and told us.

Once Mr Mate accepted that his bloodied sock prints were in the house he tried to explain them away by saying he returned to the house after Mr Boyfriend had killed the woman and he, Mr Mate, had accidentally walked in some of her blood while he was trying to ring the police, which he didn't manage to do. Unfortunately, what really did it for Mr Mate was the fact that he couldn't explain why he'd taken off his shoes and the trail of sock prints didn't lead to the telephone — this was in the days before mobile phones were widely available. Instead, the prints led from around the deceased out into the hall, back into the kitchen, across the kitchen floor, onto the kitchen work top, out through the kitchen window, onto the outside windowsill, down the garden path, through the side gate, down the side passageway and along the pavement away from the house. Mr Mate was found guilty of murder for more reasons than just the sock-print evidence, but the prints helped. Mr Boyfriend was also involved with the incident and his sock prints related to how he had moved around after the woman had bled to death.

✼

Another case in which I was involved need not be anonymous because it is that of David Bain. The sock-print aspect of the case related to the size of print a foot might make if it were clad in a sock that then walked in blood. It was accepted by the Crown and defence that whoever murdered the mother, two daughters and son was the same person who deposited bloodied sock prints in one of the rooms and part of the hallway of the house.

My role was relatively simple: to undertake tests with David Bain's socked feet to determine what size prints his feet would make after he walked in blood and after those marks had been enhanced with the same chemical used at the crime scene in 1994 by the Crown's expert. This evidence was important in the retrial because the Privy Council had referred to the sock-print evidence as being one of the reasons they considered a substantial miscarriage of justice had occurred.

By way of background, a forensic scientist and a police officer examined the carpets for the presence of blood. They detected a number of bloodied sock prints, made by a right foot, on the carpet leading from Stephen Bain's room, into Margaret Bain's room, tracking out into the hallway. The carpet on which the sock prints were located was not retained and as far as we know it went up in smoke when the house was burnt down.

The sock prints were on a dark-coloured carpet and a chemical called luminol was used to enhance them. Luminol reacts with iron in blood, causing a blue alien-like glow that can last for a few minutes. In fact, when I was measuring the test sock prints, I remember glancing around the floor of the laboratory at the eerie scene of disembodied prints heading in all different directions and being surprised at how long the glow lasted. As the glow fades after five minutes or so, it's one of those lights that looks brighter from the corner of your eye.

Some of the sock prints at Every Street were incomplete but two were described by the forensic scientist who examined them as being 280 mm long, *that the print encompassed both the heel and the toes, that was a complete print from heel to toe.* This evidence he repeated: *The other prints that I detected with luminol showed the toes as well, taken from the top of the toes to the heel.*

The simple question was whether or not David Bain's foot could have made marks of that size and description. Although David Bain testified in evidence at the first trial that he had gone from room to room after he got home, the sock prints were found in a place where the Crown case said Robin Bain would never had been on that morning. At the first trial it was accepted that the sock prints had been made by David although it's not clear why that happened. It could have been because evidence was given that:

> ... *socks taken to be Robin's were measured at 240 mm, and socks taken to be David's were measured at 270 mm. Evidence was given of the inside measurements of their respective shoes, showing Robin's at 275 mm and David's at 304 mm ... the jury were not told ... that Robin's feet had been measured in the mortuary and found to be 270 mm.*

> Privy Council ruling, 2007

A forensic scientist for the Crown undertook some bloodied sock-print tests in 1997 and 2007; the final results of these tests were described as follows:

> ... *that a walking person with a 300 mm foot, making sock prints with the sock completely bloodied, would be expected to make a print greater than 280 mm.*
>
> [However] ... *a print of about 280 mm could be made* [and further] ... *if a 280 mm print were made by a completely bloodied sole of a 300 mm foot, then the print must be incomplete to the extent of 20 mm. Therefore a portion from the tip of the toes, or the end of the heel, or both, must be missing from the print.*

In response to this work, the forensic scientist who had attended Every Street made a further statement saying that his description of *a complete print from heel to toe at 280 mm* meant that in the print he could see the toe area as well as the heel area, to differentiate it from other partial prints.

Hence the sock-print tests described in the Prologue. The tests we conducted used methods applied by the Crown's expert. The results of my tests indicated that David Bain's foot was too big to deposit complete marks 280 mm long. His feet are 300 mm long and he deposited luminol-enhanced marks that were, on average, 306 mm long. This was an average taken from a total of 22 prints, which ranged from 300 mm to 315 mm.

Chapter 15

The police

In order for sense and sanity to prevail in a world full of chaos, anger and loss, there have to be ways of managing jobs like mine and those of people who are more directly involved with crime. Either let the emotions out and hope they go away or bottle them up until they escape of their own accord in ways that can't be predicted. For me, it's pressure release through humour. Although the accounts in this chapter are tragic in their own way, there is an edge of humour to many of them and they should be read on that basis. I'm not trying to belittle anyone or make light of any given situations; rather I hope to demonstrate that people in what would otherwise often be unbearably serious situations do, and say, funny things. And when you work with people all the time, I think it's nice to acknowledge these funny things. When they're read out of context and in the cold light of day, you have to wonder about how the events appeared at the material time. For further comment by the police on the job of the police, I suggest reading *Wasting Police Time: the crazy world of the war on crime* by PC David Copperfield (it's not his real name but it stops him getting lynched by various parties). At this point, I should add that despite the glares and dirty looks I sometimes get as an independent expert, I have a huge respect for most police officers. They have an extremely challenging work life and they see the absolute worst of the human race.

There has been criticism that literacy and numeracy standards in the English police have dropped over the years and I have to say that in some circumstances I do wonder how particular officers passed their exams. Read this and decide what it says:

> **Reason doctor requested:** *banage on left rist and grase to his nee. We are lead to be leave that he has taken drugs with drink.*

Remind me again, who's taken the drugs with drink?

There are also many set ways of doing things within police forces, for the sake of clarity and continuity. You can always spot an independent fingerprint examiner as being a former police officer, because they always write people's surnames in CAPITAL letters.

The police are taught to handle any kind of situation and they have ways of dealing with difficult, drunk, drugged-up, belligerent people. They also have a duty of care and to ensure that the people they hold in custody don't come to any harm and that if there is any suggestion a person is ill, medical assistance is sought. Excess alcohol consumption can potentially be fatal. If sufficient is consumed then a person can lose the ability to coordinate their muscles to such an extent that they stop breathing. It's called 'respiratory arrest'. So it's important that the police establish if someone truly is at risk, or if they've got a faker on their hands. This extract shows an example of how they can manage to make the distinction:

When I approached him, he opened his eyes, looked at me and then closed his eyes again. I tried to raise SMITH by talking to him and he started to wake up initially but then he mumbled something which I did not understand and then seemed to go back to sleep. I then tried to wake SMITH by pressing on his right ear lobe to create a pain response and make him more alert. SMITH immediately woke up when I pressed his ear lobe and tried to grab my arm. He mumbled something to the effect of 'LEAVE ME ALONE' and tried to go back to sleep.

That's polite police speak for *he was faking it so I pinched his ear good and hard to get a reaction. I got one and he told me to sod off.*

The interesting circumstances of this case are that Mr Smith was found slumped at the controls of a mobility scooter he'd stolen from outside a local supermarket. Just a quick note here: Mobility scooters are incredibly common in certain parts of England, particularly the flat parts. In the town where I lived at the time, there was one old guy who drove his scooter everywhere, including down the main roads into town, down the country lanes and on the bypass around the next town over. He never stopped for traffic lights, pedestrian crossings or cars. What made it yet more interesting is that his scooter had no indicators so if he had to cut across traffic or make a turn, he just stuck his arm out and off he went. The problem was, he only had one arm so you never knew when he was going to turn right.

Anyway, back to Mr Smith, who was so drunk he couldn't be bothered to walk home, hence the reason for acquisition of a form of transport. Unfortunately, he passed out while he was driving his stolen mobility scooter off down the road, as he made what was probably not the fastest getaway in history. When the police caught up with him, presumably at a slow jog, and checked the front basket of the scooter, they found a half-full pint glass of beer. Not only was he drunk in charge of a mobility scooter, he'd actually been drinking on the job.

More police-speak was apparent in another case where the final line of the statement very casually stated that *the defendant was taken to his cell where due to his demeanour and threats he was strip-searched.* There were no more details on his demeanour that had caused this occurrence but I can only assume that he must have upset them in a major way.

Perhaps our previous defendant had upset the police but this next one must have made them wonder why they even bother. In this case, the police describe how a car left the road, failed to negotiate a road junction, demolished three street signs in the process and came to rest in a field on the other side of a ditch approximately 10 feet wide and six feet deep. This is police-speak for *he drove like the clappers, missed the junction and was going so fast he flew over a 10-foot-wide ditch and landed in a field.* The police officer approached the car and asked the driver if he was alright, to which he received an obscene gynaecological description of himself. Why indeed would you bother? And please don't say that his outburst could have been some stress response to the accident because I read the rest of the case circumstances and his behaviour towards the police did not improve — he was just rude.

When someone in England and Wales is required to provide breath samples to an evidential breath-testing device (the one they have at the police station), the police input the name of the person who is providing the breath samples using a keyboard at the start of the testing procedure. This is so the police don't get accused of adding someone's name to the wrong printout at a later time. The person who provided the breath samples is then asked if they want to receive a copy of the printout for their own records and they are also asked to sign all three copies (one for the subject, two for police paperwork). The three printouts from the device then have all the details of the test including the name, gender and date of birth details the subject provided to the police at the start of the breath-testing procedure, along with their breath alcohol results and some other bits and pieces. In one case, the man in question informed the police he had been arrested 76 times, which is probably how he justified carrying three metal bars in his car, although I doubt any magistrate or judge would be best impressed.

When asked his name so it could be entered into the breath-testing device, he answered FUCKOFFFINDITOUTFOR-YOURSELF. Just all charm some people. Quite accurately and appropriately in the circumstances I think, the officer referred to the defendant as Mr FUCKOFFFINDITOUT-FORYOURSELF all the way through his statement and also when giving evidence at court, because it was the only name he had at the time.

Yet other members of the general public must either make or break a police officer's night shift. Imagine this: you're on patrol when you see some drunk bloke at a petrol station who's driven his vehicle into a concrete curb. He's so drunk he can't get out of the car so you go and help. The driver's committed an offence (drink driving) so you arrest him. According to the police statement, during the course of the arrest the driver (who becomes the defendant by the time I get involved) stopped using his legs, either because of alcohol paralysis or stubbornness, so he was *lowered to the ground*. After they eventually manage to get him to the police station, officers then tried to get the defendant to go from the car to the custody desk. He refused to walk so he had to be dragged which, the officer pointed out, seemed strange: ... *as when I had left him with the other officers, he was struggling and shouting at police. He was taken straight through towards the cells but then was laid on the floor for the Custody Sergeant to review him medically. The defendant was refusing to respond to anything said to him but was conscious as he responded to pain.*

An ambulance was called and when the ambulance crew arrived, the defendant was still refusing to cooperate and was rolling around on the floor holding his head. The police officer was again surprised when he turned up at the hospital to see the defendant being taken through Casualty in a wheelchair, smiling and chatting to the nurses. The defendant was then put in a bed in a cubicle on his own. The officer said in his statement that, *at one point, he was in the cubicle on his own and I was a short distance away. I saw him lift his head and look around. He then lay back down again before lifting himself over the side rail of the bed and throwing himself onto the ground. He did this on two occasions. It led me to believe that he was trying to get our attention.*

On other occasions, I seriously wonder how officers keep a straight face. It's one thing to write something in a statement; it's an entirely different thing to have to get up in court and say it out loud. But it has to be done because detail is everything. For example:

ZEBEDEE was dressed as a woman in a sweater, short skirt, fishnet tights and high heeled boots. His face was made up; he had lipstick on and a blonde wig. He said he would like to be addressed as ZEBEDEE. His mood was low but he had good eye contact.

Here's an example of when the police must seriously have had a good chuckle back at the station: police attended the relevant location after receiving a report from a member of the public that a drunk woman was trying to drive a car away from a supermarket car park on a Monday afternoon. When the police approached the car, they found the defendant sitting in the driver's seat, naked from the waist down and wearing a white top pulled up exposing her breasts. When she spoke, she was very difficult to understand and was apparently VERY drunk (their emphasis). When asked what she had been doing, she slurred, 'Shagging', although she was on her own in the car.

Police officers, particularly those who have been in the job for a while, often have that look about them that says, *I've seen it all and nothing surprises me any more.* Imagine the thought processes of an officer who attended the scene of a crashed vehicle that was badly damaged. As he approached, the officer noticed two men sitting inside. When asked what they were doing, they replied that they were helping the owner by taking out the radio and speakers before they were stolen. When asked who owned the car, they were unsure.

As I said before, the police have a tough job, and sometimes it's physically demanding, as in the instance when two officers in a patrol car encountered a man slumped over the steering wheel of his car. The police knocked on the side window to try to raise a response. Calls to dispatch helped establish the man's name and that the car was parked on his own front lawn. The driver was unable to move, walk, talk or even crawl to the police car and, although it may seem unnecessary, the officers decided to call for backup. A riot van with two more officers duly arrived. It transpired that this wasn't because of the risk of the driver becoming violent but because he was 21 stone (133 kg). He couldn't be manoeuvred into the back of a patrol car so he had to be placed on a riot shield and dragged across the lawn.

The stories the police have are many and varied and not all of them can be told. Their jobs aren't getting any easier but I hope for their sakes they can remember the lighter side of things when they get the chance.

Chapter 16

The case of the heebie-jeebies

A friend of mine does far more crime scene attendance than me. One of the worst cases for him was turning up at a murder scene to find that the victim looked just like his wife. It was years ago but he still remembers it, clear as day.

We all have them: the cases that cause a sort of mental trauma and therefore refuse to leave your head and also refuse to be shoved into the dark box in the recess of your mind where you store all the really worrying, scary stuff. When I say 'we', I mean anyone who has to deal with any kind of trauma. People have different standards of what qualifies as an event or occasion for the Dark Box of the Mind but people involved with suffering and trauma must have a larger box than a lot of other people. I guess a psychologist would be better placed to talk about the whys and wherefores, but that's not me; I just know that people in front-line positions, like medics, police, CSIs and forensic scientists, often need access to a psychologist or sometimes just need to know that there's one there to help, if need be. There are of course plenty of other people who need psychological assistance to deal with an enormous range of issues but before anyone says I've missed these people out, I'm just talking about the arena of forensic science.

As an independent forensic scientist in England, the issue of receiving help to deal with particularly traumatic cases wasn't one that needed to occur very often. However, when your day-to-day job involves tripping around the countryside collecting fly pupae off rotting corpses, sometimes the circumstances get to you and every now and then you need help dealing with the disgustingness of it.

For whatever reason, the heebee-jeebies cases literally haunt you, even during the day. It's similar to when you're reading a really, really good book and you become so immersed in it you take on the emotions of the character and the story. I used to do that a lot when I was reading *Rachel's Holiday* by Marian Keyes. Rachel was angry a lot in parts of that book and I used to carry it into my real life, where the real people, like my partner, lived. Poor bloke. He had long hair at the time, like the main man in *Rachel's Holiday*. He got a lot of stick in the days when I was reading about the main character, Rachel, having to hear from her beau what she'd been like as a drug and alcohol addict. Not that I have ever been either, but still, I carried that rage with me throughout the day and the sense of loss when I finished reading that book was palpable — it left me with a big empty hole of disappointment in the pit of my stomach.

If that's what it's like after reading a work of fiction, imagine how it can feel if you allow emotion to enter into your casework. I don't consciously allow it. I don't personalise cases and I don't think about them in anything but clinical, scientific terms. My job is to solve a problem using science and that's exactly what I set out to do. I have it easier than other people involved in this game because of my distance from the actual cold, hard events. Nevertheless, every now and then a case gets through the armour and lodges itself in the soft underbelly of your consciousness.

Someone I know was attending only her second post-mortem, a case where the body of a 17-year-old girl had been exhumed from beneath the floor of a house. Even though the body had been underground for years, because it had been wrapped in rubbish bags it was still partially preserved. She said she has never lost the memory of the skin on the nape of the victim's neck, because it looked so complete and lifelike. She immediately thought of her own child, who was also 17 at that time.

In July 2005 I attended a training course in London. Just days earlier, some of the people on the course had been the first fire officers on the scenes of the London Tube bombings and the Tavistock Road bus bomb. Their faces said it all. Then you add into the equation the information that people who were running the course had their offices in Tavistock Square and their offices were currently crime scenes. They'd had crime scene examiners taking biological swabs from their desks. The results would not only help determine the mechanics of the explosion but potentially identify some of the victims. Think about what it would be like to have that to remember every time you sat at your desk in future. This was also a problem in 2001, after the World Trade Centre destruction. Sometimes, victims can only be identified by their vaporised remains; tops of adjacent buildings had to be checked for body parts and it's someone's job to go and do that collecting.

With some cases, it's easy to predict when they're likely to cause problems. For me, it's usually the ones involving young children. Like the children who die of methadone overdoses because their parents were too wasted to keep it out of the child's way, or the children who suffer abuse at the hands of those who are supposed to protect them. I know that someone has to do these cases because otherwise the justice system isn't working properly, but if I have a choice, I occasionally say no, grateful of having the luxury of being able to choose my cases. Having said that, recently I worked on a case involving the death of a toddler in unusual circumstances (was he pushed or did he fall?) and it hasn't caused me any problems.

There doesn't seem to be any rhyme or reason to how my mind selects cases to use for mental torture; it's just a lottery. For example, I remember that when two-year-old Aisling Symes disappeared from an Auckland suburb in October 2009, I could barely watch the news — the pain of the family was palpable and I was feeling it with them. Perhaps it was because the media portrayal was designed to be emotive, or perhaps I was simply caught off-guard.

When it was announced after seven days that Aisling had been found dead in a storm drain, the police family liaison officer had to break it to the waiting media. Here was a man, a police officer, whose job it was to tell the parents their child was dead, then go and tell the press, all the time not being allowed to show emotion, just be strong, impartial, being an information transfer point, a representative of the police force. Understandably, and in my mind, entirely to his credit, he struggled to hold it together in that press announcement. He is trained to do an incredibly difficult job and carry that burden with the family — and then go and do it again next week for someone else. No matter what we think we understand about some people's jobs, it sometimes pales into insignificance with what they actually have to do.

The thing with the cases that stick with you and have an emotional impact is that there is never any clue when they're coming. You just pick up a case file one day and it leaps out at you. And no matter what you do, it's like a leech sticking to part of your memory bank. Even the cases you know you don't want to do. I remember a case in England where a baby had been kicked to death and our company was instructed to do a review for the defence. Having just had a baby, I could no more do that case than fly a plane, so I passed it off to a colleague with some feeble excuse about having so many court appointments coming up I didn't have time. I don't regret passing on that case, but I haven't forgotten it either, and all I read were the first two paragraphs of the solicitor's letter of enquiry.

There are several other cases that will never leave me for one reason or another. The one that has stuck because of the 'it-took-me-by-surprise' element is from 2008 and involved a triple murder that had occurred the previous July in Manchester. A 36-year-old mother and her two children, an 18-year-old daughter and a 13-year-old son, were bludgeoned to death with an engineer's hammer. The two females had been sexually assaulted. No one really knows who died first but the son's body was found covered with a duvet on the floor next to his mother's bed — this is the image I just can't escape, that sits as a static frame in my mind's eye.

It was an enormously involved case, which included two days

examining items at the Crown's forensic science laboratory. It didn't help matters that it was the furthest lab from where I worked. It was a two-person job so my boss came with me. It was dark and cold, being February in northern England. We were looking at the footwear mark aspect of the case because a lot of the upstairs floors in the house of the deceased had not been carpeted, which meant good surfaces for recording footwear marks. In all, we examined several marks, a blood-stained carpet and some shoes. I didn't see a single crime scene photo depicting any of the deceased *in situ* and I didn't see any postmortem photos, but for some reason, the image of that child next to his mother's bed is strong as strong can be.

Another case I will never forget was a murder that took place in London. For months, it held nothing more than a scientific interest; I was looking at the footwear aspect of the case and whether the defendant had been where he said he'd been in the house. The reason I now remember that case is because a colleague worked on the blood pattern aspect. He mentioned one of the postmortem photographs that had disturbed him. Up until that point, neither the case nor the photographs, including the one in question, had bothered me and none of them had made it past my sophisticated mental filtration system. The reason the case got through and lodged in my mind is because the filtration system wasn't activated at the time the mental breakthrough was made; I was on the phone with this colleague who had reviewed the blood pattern aspect of the case but we were talking about something entirely different. The case had obviously got into his brain and something in our conversation made him mention that one postmortem photograph. Since then, I can't think of a blood pattern case without an image of the victim's front hallway and that one postmortem photo popping into my head. Thanks for that, colleague mate!

Occasionally, it's not the actual case that gives you the heebie-jeebies, it's the people involved. I attended court once for a drink-drive case. The issue was about whether or not the police officer should have requested a second breath-screening sample from the defendant: the first time she tried, the screening device she was using was dodgy and came up with a pass, but because the driver stank so badly of alcohol she asked a colleague to lend her the breath-screening unit from his patrol car, which he did. The defendant provided a further breath sample, which registered a fail. This gave the police officer the authority to require the defendant to accompany her to the nearest police station where he would be required to provide an evidential breath test, blood test or both. The breath samples he provided at the police station were both *way* over the legal limit and, from an analytical point of view, there was nothing wrong with them. As far as I could see, the defendant had been caught drink driving, end of story.

The solicitor, on the other hand, was running a technical argument about the legality of the basis on which his client had been arrested. If he could convince the court that the police officer had unlawfully acquired the second sample of breath to the screening device then the damning evidential breath tests undertaken at the police station would not be admissible as evidence and his client wouldn't be guilty of anything.

All he wanted me to do was say that the first breath-screening device was operating perfectly well at the time his client provided the breath sample, which meant he could argue his case with a good chance of winning. The thing was, at the time he was asking me this question I was in an interview room at the court, which had no windows and the window in the door was covered over. No one knew I was in there; no one had seen me go in because it was a very quiet court and everyone was having a tea break. The client, his dad and the solicitor stood between me and freedom beyond the door. It made me feel very uncomfortable, particularly as they weren't going to like anything I had to say because I thought the first breath-testing device *had* been malfunctioning (based on paperwork I had received about it) and that there was nothing wrong with the defendant being asked to provide a second sample for a screening test. So what did I do? I made vague comments to the solicitor that sounded reasonably helpful and then suggested we get a cup of tea, seeing as everyone else was on tea break. Once we'd made it out of the door, I firmed up my vague view that there wasn't a leg to stand on from the defence point of view, and scarpered across the foyer where I could see the security guards. Needless to say I didn't give evidence in that case. Never again have I gone into an interview room without at least some fuss or a hot cup of tea as a defence or distraction.

Until I give up this work, I will have to deal with the difficult aspects of cases such as those briefed above or the others that aren't for general consumption. It's part of the job, I accept that and I know how to deal with it; the enjoyment and the sense of achievement I get far outweigh the negatives. I just hope that my old age isn't dogged by remnant images.

Chapter 17

David Bain

... the evidence is being re-presented in court, and tiny portions of it drip-fed to us day-by-day ... This does give the impression, though, that there are millions of viewers and readers who are now the jury and not the 12 citizens chosen for the task. Of course we would have to hear, see and read all the evidence presented before making judgment. In theory the facts presented to us daily are objective. Yet they are chosen to frame a story about the case.

Mark Houlahan talking about the David Bain
retrial, *Waikato Times*, 21 March 2009

Mr Bain has now been acquitted and Mr Karam vindicated. The latter has won almost as many detractors as admirers for his dogged pursuit of the case, but there would be few who would not welcome his aid if they found themselves convicted of a crime they did not commit.

Dominion Post, 9 June 2009

The clock on the wall says 4.43 p.m. and it's all over. Or maybe it's just heading in a new direction.

The Bain case is kind of a Kiwi institution. It's never really gone away since 20 June 1994, when five members of the Bain family were found dead and one family member was stretchered from the family home. David Bain was tried and convicted in May 1995, then sentenced in June 1995 to life imprisonment with a minimum 16 years non-parole period. He appealed the conviction but before the appeal process was completed, the police had arranged for destruction of many samples that had been collected in relation to their investigation. The house itself was burnt to the ground by the fire service, under direction from the wider Bain family, in unexpectedly dramatic fashion 17 days after the deaths themselves, just over a week after David Bain had been charged. Destruction of the house made national news as footage of enormous flames and billowing smoke were filmed from a helicopter.

The Bain family lived at 65 Every Street, Dunedin, New Zealand, where they had been living since their return from Papua New Guinea a few years earlier. At the time of death, father Robin was aged 58, mother Margaret was aged 50, elder son David was 22, elder daughter Arawa was 19, younger daughter Laniet was 18 and younger son Stephen was 14 years of age. Robin was the principal of Taieri Mouth Primary School, a small two-teacher school approximately 50 kilometres south along the coast from Dunedin. Margaret didn't work. David was a Music and Classics student at the University of Otago, Arawa was in her second year of teacher training, Laniet had lived in Dunedin and Stephen was attending Bayfield High School. Margaret and Robin were estranged, although this was not widely known at the time. Robin returned to the Every Street house at weekends, although he didn't sleep in the house itself, instead sleeping in a caravan in the back garden.

All of the events that relate to David Bain's arrest, convictions, imprisonment, appeals, hearings, retrial and subsequent release following five not guilty verdicts stem from the events of that now long ago morning. This chapter is not about what happened on that day or the events that occurred up until I became involved. It is also not about particular issues that formed any part of the case for either side. This is solely about what I experienced.

My decision to become involved with the case was very closely considered. Admittedly, that decision involved a degree of naivety because I had no appreciation of the depth of feeling about the case: I wasn't here at the time of the killings or the first trial so none of the milestones between 1994 and 2008 meant anything to me. When I was first contacted about the case by a colleague, I had never heard of either David Bain (who?) or Joe Karam (double who?) — what are the chances of that in a country the size of New Zealand?

My involvement with the David Bain case came completely by chance and totally out of the blue. I first met Joe Karam in the office of the Coffee Guy in Auckland, a company he founded but that is now owned by one of his sons, with a business partner. I was invited along to the meeting by a colleague because I hadn't long been back in the country after a six-year absence, and I wanted to get back into forensic science as soon as I could.

As the meeting started, this man across the table was staring at us in much the same way as a hawk eyes up a rabbit. It was an all-piercing stare and, quite frankly, was bloody uncomfortable. A large book of photographs was thrust across the table at me and the man on the other side of the table started talking about blood smears, spatter patterns and gunshot wounds, flicking constantly between the 700-odd pages to point out things and compare them with others. There was a huge amount of information to try to absorb in a short space of time.

I felt as if I was lagging behind because these two men clearly had *far* more idea about this case than me. This isn't necessarily an unusual situation: by the time an independent forensic scientist is called in to work on a case, the lawyers who are calling have usually had weeks, if not months, to become familiar with the circumstances. It's not uncommon for them to forget how much they know, whereas the first the scientist heard about it was three minutes ago. So playing catch-up is normal and the best way for me to deal with it is to suggest that a copy of the relevant paperwork and photographs be sent to me so I can peruse them, absorb what they mean and come up with a coherent plan of action based on what I've been given.

In this first meeting with Joe Karam, I felt like a sitting duck as I was sized up for my suitability to become involved with this case. He eventually decided my CV didn't indicate that I'd be of any use to him and the meeting was over.

I assumed that was it and chalked it up to experience, but then the phone rang a few days' later and it was Joe Karam asking if I knew any pathologists or blood spatter experts in

England who might be prepared to have a look at a case in New Zealand. As it happens, I know a fair few experts in England and they have exactly that kind of experience, as well as lots more. So I hung up the phone after saying I'd check with my colleagues and get back to him. A Skype phone call later and the answer from England was, yes, they'd be happy to look at the case to see what assistance they could offer.

First refusal for the pathology was going to Dr Chapman, the man who did the postmortems of Princess Diana and Dodi Al Fayed. Although I was slightly uncomfortable with the thought of having to see him again after I'd so rudely fainted in his mortuary on a previous occasion, it was an excellent opportunity to bring some world-class skills to New Zealand. That was the point when I made the decision about whether or not to get involved — if experts from the United Kingdom were going to be consulted then the defence team would need someone with scientific knowledge to be the liaison between England and New Zealand. And so it began.

That first meeting at the Coffee Guy led to the involvement of the following defence experts from the United Kingdom:

- Dr Robert Chapman, Home Office pathologist who'd examined approximately 2000 cases of suspicious and homicidal death and approximately 18,000 sudden deaths (that's a lot of dead bodies), renowned not only for his involvement with the Diana and Dodi case, but also as the supervising pathologist for the 2007 London Tube bombings.
- Dr John Manlove, having been a Crown expert in the United Kingdom with particular expertise in

blood spatter, DNA, sample collection and storage, entomology (insects) and crime scene examination, now running his own consultancy and involved with many high-profile cases including crime scenes and deaths in Iraq and central Europe.

- Carl Lloyd, former police officer with over 25 years' experience as a fingerprint examiner, including time spent in the USA and Abu Dhabi.
- Philip Boyce, firearms expert of 20-plus years with time spent in the Territorial Army in Northern Ireland during the Troubles of the 1970s and 1980s, with knowledge and expertise in terrorism and major incidents including time spent in Iraq and Afghanistan.

It's a pretty impressive skill base and yet they represent only a small selection of the skills available, which is why I feel justified in saying that if a case needs an expert with certain skills, I'm pretty sure I know someone.

Once I'd made the decision to become involved with the Bain case, it was like opening a door and walking into the eye of a hurricane. Once the door was shut, there was no turning round and opening it again. I worked in the eye of the storm for six months, blissfully unaware of what was swirling around me. I had no idea of the strength of the hurricane until the retrial started, by which time it was too late to get out of the way. If you spend any time thinking about it, which I don't usually, it can be a daunting task to be up against the might of the Crown. In this case, my strong impression was that there were 14 years of bad feeling running through the country, of which neither I nor the experts I involved were aware until we were actually in Christchurch. For me, a case should always be impersonal; this is work, we are professionals and I have been trained to expect all involved to deal with it the same way.

There are three questions I am now often asked. I've already answered the first, *Is your job like CSI?* The second is, *So go on then, you were there, is he guilty or not?* When people ask me this question, it's not because they want to know what *I* think. It's because they want to tell me what they think, which they usually do whether I want to hear it or not. The third is, *What was it like being part of the David Bain retrial?* That is a question I *can* answer. Make your mind a blank canvas and draw a picture as we go along.

My involvement with the pretrial aspect of the case was quite extensive. Once I'd convinced the British experts to have a look at this case, I then told them how much work would actually be involved and that there was so much documentation I'd have to ship most of it over in a large storage box. The rest would be delivered by hand. Some of it was taken by Joe Karam, who combined the trip with a Privy Council hearing and de-brief with the experts concerned. The items that were going to be examined in England were hand-delivered by a police officer at the insistence of the Crown, which is fair enough. I have no idea how they decided who got to go, but I imagine they wouldn't have been short of volunteers.

I spent many, *many* hours reading documents, photocopying, setting up files, deciding what was relevant for the experts and reviewing documents that were constantly being disclosed by the Crown, right up until the time the retrial started. I spent many other hours on Skype to the experts confirming to them that, yes, lots of exhibits really had been destroyed before the appeal process had been completed; yes, the crime scene really had been burnt to the ground two weeks after the killings without retaining the carpets on which the blood-stained sock prints had been located; no, there really aren't any proper scale diagrams of some of the important things; no, certain items weren't seized at the time; no, blood really hasn't previously been identified on those items … the list goes on. From the point of view of highly experienced forensic scientists, these circumstances were, to put it bluntly, extraordinary. They were certainly highly unusual in such a serious case as a multiple murder.

Because I was already involved with the logistics of getting the expert witnesses to New Zealand and arranging videolinks for others (both experts and lay), it was a logical step to take on the logistics of getting the rest of the witnesses to court as well. That might not sound too complicated because, after all, they're grown-ups and know how to find their way around. The thing is that because the case was legally aided, all funding, including that for travel, accommodation and food, had to be approved before any tickets or hotel rooms could be booked. That meant estimating how much it would cost to get each and every witness from wherever they were in the world into Courtroom One of Christchurch High Court on the relevant date, whether it be physically or electronically. I tell you now, that is no mean feat. This was particularly so when the time estimate for the start of the defence case was a constantly moving feast, in large part dependent on the way the Crown conducted its case.

There was also the need to source experts not needed in the first trial, because of changes in the way the Crown was presenting its case in the retrial, and some of those experts had to be sourced after the retrial had started. These included the police photographer who originally photographed the fingerprints on the rifle. The Crown was saying that the fingerprints were in blood. The defence was suggesting that the fingerprints were not in blood and this was shown by the fingerprints being white-coloured against a dark background. The police photographer was required because we needed to know what sort of light had been used to enhance the fingerprints. Blood is usually enhanced using a filter and a special light, the result of which would be a photograph in which dark fingerprints appear against a lighter background. The photos of the fingerprints on the rifle actually showed the opposite situation: white fingerprints against a dark background. The police photographer confirmed he had used plain white light, which meant he hadn't used the filter that would be used if he were enhancing blood.

After many months of preparation, the retrial was finally ready to start and the media was in the starting blocks waiting for the starter's pistol. I missed it, because there was no need for me to be there. Rest assured there were plenty of other people there from the kick-off who were determined to keep the nation informed of progress, so I just watched the news.

When I finally did take a seat on the roller coaster ride that was the retrial, at the end of March, a good deal of my time was spent in court. Courtroom One of Christchurch High

Court is fairly typical of your average court and is rectangular. Entry to the main court floor is in the corner of one short side. The jury sat on one long side, two tiered rows of six seats. The judge sat to the left of the jury in what is called the bench, which was raised above the level of the main court floor at the same height as the witness box and at the opposite side from the entry door. The dock was on the opposite side of the room from the jury, facing them. The media bench (which was normally used for public seating) was off to the right of the jury, just inside and to the left of the entrance door to the court. One desk was reserved for Joe Karam — as he wasn't a lawyer and not a member of the court staff, he wasn't allowed to sit within the actual court floor. Instead he was given permission to be in court, and seated relatively close to the defence team so he could advise.

David Bain didn't sit in the dock during the trial; he was only there for the purposes of his pleas and for the verdicts. The rest of the time he sat within a few feet of the jury, facing the judge's bench but behind all counsel. Based on my many experiences in Crown and High Courts, it was slightly unusual that the court proceedings didn't seem to revolve around the defendant. Half the time you forgot he was even there, such was the performance going on around him. One media person even commented that the jury didn't seem to be in the presence of evil.

Witnesses gave evidence from the witness box, an elevated position with stairs leading up to a small, enclosed desk, with a microphone and a video screen plus a wheelie chair. The witness box faced across the main court floor to the jury so that counsel was below the level of the witness.

The witness box is a lonely and exposed position — you can almost feel the prairie winds blowing over your face, the tumbleweed rolling by and the chink of spurs as Clint Eastwood walks by, particularly during that retrial because the TV and stills camera were opposite and the black lenses were a constant reminder that everyone, literally everyone, was watching. The witness box can also be a hot and scary place, not only for people who have never given evidence before but also for experts and police officers. There were several occasions when I suspect sweaty palms were being rubbed surreptitiously on their owners' trousers or skirts.

The footage from the TV camera was beamed upstairs to the additional seating area. The footage shown up there was far more detailed than could be seen when one was actually in the main court arena. The camera randomly zoomed in on people in the court: media people texting and their facial expressions as someone sent back something amusing, views of the jury's footwear, socks and trouser bottoms as they entered and left their seats, expressions on people's faces they probably didn't think anyone could see. Some people should probably have brushed their hair a bit better. Lines on faces were far more emphasised on the TV footage than they were in real life. People tell you that being on screen adds 10 pounds to your weight; no one's ever told me it adds 10 years to your age as well.

I sat in the upstairs seating area towards the end of the defence case, after I'd given evidence, to check on how the other experts were getting on — there's no better way to learn how to improve the way you give evidence than watching other people do it. Had I known how much time the cameraman spent panning around the room, lingering on people seemingly at random, I'd probably have felt much more pressured — ignorance is bliss.

Prior to the retrial, there was much comment in the media about how the proceedings would be covered. Initially, the judge ruled that the entire proceedings could be streamed on the Internet, albeit with a 10-minute delay. I understand this was OK until it was realised that the camera wasn't turned off during a closed chambers meeting, which was held in court. As only one film camera and one stills camera were allowed in court, I assume the networks shared the footage. The whole of the chambers discussion was apparently streamed on the Internet, even though it was supposed to be private. After that, restrictions were placed on filming.

At some time during the Crown case, the instruction to the media was that they were only allowed to film David Bain for the first 15 minutes of each day. When the news was shown later that day, it sometimes showed a clip of David Bain that appeared to be contemporaneous with some piece of evidence that had just been given when, in fact, the evidence had been given at a time when the media wasn't actually filming him. Sometimes, the continuity on the news was such that people appeared to have changed their ties part way through the day's proceedings. I understand that observant trial-watchers noted these things and the question may have been discussed in the public gallery as to whether such broadcasting was an accurate record of events.

The defence team was based in an apartment hotel, which basically meant self-catering with the benefit of maid service. The accommodation was a bit of an 80s throwback and my overriding impression is one of burgundy and cold floors. Having said that, the bed was always comfy and the staff friendly, which cannot be underrated when you spend your days in the hostile environment of a criminal courtroom.

Everyone else had a 'permanent' room because they were there practically all the time, while I was moved from room to room. The main problem with that was two-fold: waking up in the morning completely disorientated because I couldn't work out where I was or where the bedroom door was — each room had a slightly different layout, and remembering which room I was in from day to day, particularly when most of my time was spent thinking about three things at once, none of which related to my room number.

The defence team also had the use of a hotel room as its war room, which was a standard hotel room swept clean of any comforts. Just inside the door was the kitchen area, which was usually festooned with abandoned coffee plungers, half-drunk cups of tea and coffee and various newspapers. The main area of the room would have contained the comfy settees, chairs and tables but they had been replaced with entirely functional albeit depressingly school-like tables pushed together to make a large work surface. There was also a copier/fax/scanner and assorted office-type requirements, including storage for the folders of the trial transcript that grew by hundreds of pages every day. Leading off the main room was what would have been the bedroom but was kitted out with shelves and dozens of large A4 folders, piles of papers, a desk and a couple of chairs. This was my refuge area when discussions at the main table became intense and I couldn't escape out of the main door.

I was up and down to Christchurch throughout the trial, usually coming home at weekends. When I was down in Christchurch the hours were long and seemingly unending. The team in which I had been temporarily seconded was an interesting mixture of morning people (Joe Karam, Helen Cull), evening people (Matt Karam, me), all-the-time people (Paul Morten), and Michael Reed, who did either or both ends of the day, depending on circumstances. The thing is that although each person had a preference for the time of day they would have liked to work, the trial did not allow for that choice, so everyone worked all the time.

A typical day for me involved getting up at about 7 a.m. and having a quick breakfast while reading a list of things I had prepared the night before of what had to be done before court commenced for the day. At about 7.30 a.m. I'd head uncertainly into the fray of the war room. Sometimes it was a quiet place because a meeting was already being held somewhere else but usually it was a stampede of activity with everyone trying to get things done, whether it be photocopying, faxing, telephone calls, discussing the day ahead or all of the above at once. That sounds chaotic but it had an underlying structure where everyone had jobs to do and they did them.

David Bain would arrive at around 8.30 a.m., which brought some calm to the place; at the end of the day, the defence team was there to present a case in court on his behalf so the morning was when he made his quiet opinions about matters known to the team. What I will say is that he was very well mannered and polite and he seemed to understand that I couldn't really talk to him because it wasn't my job and it just isn't the 'done thing'. That made me feel bad because I'm not naturally a rude person but in this situation, it wasn't appropriate for me to be anything else. I didn't even think it would be appropriate for me to explain that to him, so I just had to feel uncomfortable about it and he just had to put up with it. I usually made myself scarce for the morning conflabs — not really my place to be there for all that and it gave me an excuse to be away from the room and not appear rude.

Someone would then walk David Bain across to the court and deliver him into the hands of the court security. I think I walked him over twice when there was no one else available and we managed to get there without talking about anything apart from the weather. The departure of David Bain to court meant there was very little time left to finish preparing whatever it was, so there'd be a revitalised flourish of activity and the next thing you knew, they'd all be gone, leaving papers floating through the air, coming to rest like feathers in the cold silence. I say cold silence not because the silence felt cold but because it was *so* cold in the room. I wore my slippers all the time at the hotel because the concrete floors were so cold, even though they were carpeted. Why New Zealand hasn't taken wholeheartedly to central heating, double glazing and insulation I will never know.

After a quick scurry across the quadrant to the court building, which, incidentally, is a horrible brown monstrosity that would give some English urban planners a run for their money, grabbing a quick cuppa from the coffee shop and settling into the courtroom, the day's activities would begin.

I often wondered whether court observers, like the media or people in the public gallery, could tell when a day of contention was ahead. Unlike its portrayal on TV, trial progression can be a tedious and ponderous series of events. Information has to be read out so that it's recorded on tape as part of the court record. In this case, the audio tapes were electronically sent to Auckland, at the other end of the country, where they were typed up and then sent back down to Christchurch for someone to print out and distribute the dozens of pages generated daily. Sometimes, all the lawyers disappeared off for a closed chambers meeting, leaving the rest of us sitting about waiting for something to happen. On some days, though, we knew before we got to court that the day ahead would be tense, interesting, nerve-wracking and sometimes unpredictable. On those days, the air felt prickly and there was little or no eye contact between members of the opposite legal teams. How tuned in were the media people to the atmosphere? Could they tell something juicy was coming? I don't know because I never really spoke to any of them but I'd be interested to find out.

At 11.30 a.m. there was a coffee break, which involved someone hurtling across the road to gather supplies from the coffee shop and then everyone piling into a reserved room for a quick discussion about progress, then back into the court for the rest of the morning session. Lunch itself was usually a hurried affair with much discussion and debate, run back to court for the afternoon session, with a coffee break for intense discussions at about 3.30 p.m. and then finish court for the day at around five.

If only that had been where it ended, but that was when the real work of the day usually began. A de-brief was held for an hour or so until hunger drove everyone away before we reconvened at about 7.30 p.m. for more planning and discussion. Tasks assigned, most people dispersed to go and meet other people or to work on issues. Paul Morten and Matt Karam were usually wandering in and out of the war room until the early hours of the morning, dealing with legal technicalities.

Then it was up again at 7 o'clock the following morning to start all over again. Bear in mind that that was just *my* hourly input. It wasn't unusual for people to have only a few hours' sleep and spend the rest of the time preparing documents — because we all know that document preparation is a hugely time-costly exercise.

I also had most of the weekends off, whereas the defence team mostly worked seven days a week for the duration of the trial. It was just as well it ran over Easter so that everyone on all sides had a break.

The protocol for running a criminal trial dictates that the Crown has to make available to the defence the information on which it is going to rely for its case. That's the way the New Zealand justice system works and it means there shouldn't be any unexpected surprises from the Crown during presentation of their side of the case. However, there were several times when the Crown's experts went 'off brief', which meant they started being asked questions by Crown prosecutors about things that hadn't previously been mentioned and therefore the defence didn't know were going to crop up.

This was an aspect of the way the case was run that was new to me; in England there would never be any question of a witness being allowed to talk about something new without the other side being given at least a week's notice. The upshot was some full-on, late-night hours on the phone to England discussing new issues and getting copies of documents to experts and receiving comments back. Despite that, by far the most intense time for me was when the defence case was presented.

During the time that the prosecution presented its case, the atmosphere in the courtroom between the two sides had been relatively friendly and as relaxed as could be expected. Banter was usually relatively light. It is normal for the Crown case to take the most amount of time and the defence reacts to issues as they arise but as soon as the prosecution case ended and the defence case started, the atmosphere switched. It was more oppressive, darker and there was no edge of softness about it. It seemed to me that the prosecution didn't like the idea of a lengthy defence case; there were 50-plus witnesses, which is far more than average. It was the prosecution's turn to be reactionary.

In most trials, the type of pressure on each of the teams changes at the swap-over point. The whole experience of this case, for me, was mentally and physically exhausting, and I felt hugely responsible for the expert witnesses from England I had dragged into the case. To me, the coverage throughout the retrial felt generally negative towards the defence and I was worried that they would suffer at the hands of the media, which would be unexpected for them. In England, everyone accepts that expert witnesses are there for the benefit of the court, not those instructing them, so the media doesn't generally give them grief and the opposition team treats them with respect. For whatever reason, this didn't seem to me to be the case in this trial, so I was worried about that. Surprisingly, I wasn't worried about giving my own evidence; the trial had been going on for so long by that point that I just wanted to get it over and done with.

The day I gave evidence, the weather was cold and wet with intermittent hailstorms. I sat outside the courtroom with two lay witnesses and talked to them in general terms about what it's like to give evidence in court. *Yes, you can sit down; no, it's nothing like it is on CSI.*

Then the court door opened and the clerk said, 'Dr Anna Sandiford', which never fails to set off a small voice in my head that says, *Remind me again, why do I do this job?* The walk up to the witness box is always the hardest part because everyone watches you. Then you have to climb the stairs, open your briefcase, get out your papers, take the oath and face the crowd. Nothing feels more real. It's raw and cold and there's no way back.

The evidence I gave in the Bain retrial is described in an earlier chapter about sock prints. As far as giving evidence goes, the Bain retrial was no different from any other trial.

Nothing about the actual experience stands out as being any different from any other case, including the weather, apart from being able to sit down, but that's a bonus not a detraction. I have to say, though, that despite being in Christchurch on and off for three months, the photo in the paper of me giving evidence was not the best I've ever seen. But then I always dislike photos of myself.

Of course, one of the main things that sticks in my mind was the day of the verdicts. I wasn't sure whether I should stay around for the verdicts but I figured that I'd invested a lot of time and energy in the case and it would make a change to actually wait for the conclusion rather than hotfooting it off home at the first opportunity. So, despite not being on the clock any more, I decided that another day or so in Christchurch wouldn't matter. As long as I was home by Saturday for a family gathering it would be fine.

I sat through a day and a half of the judge's summing up, which was more than I had expected and clearly far more than the public in the TV viewing room had expected because there was a lot of fidgeting and muttering along the lines of *Get on with it.* The judge finished his summing up in the afternoon of 4 June and the jury chose not to start their deliberations that evening but to come back the next day. So, on Friday morning everyone gathered in court as normal, there was a bit of legal procedure and then the jury went off to the jury room just about morning tea time, which left a whole load of us, including media, standing there trying to decide what to do. It was anticlimactic.

I went back to my hotel room and tried to watch TV but couldn't settle, so I went into the war room to try and pack some boxes of files, but couldn't settle to that either. Eventually, I ended up going round the Rita Angus exhibition, which was showing at the Christchurch Gallery, with Paul Morten and his wife, Anna, until mid-afternoon of a beautiful sunny day. We were in the middle of the exhibition when Paul's phone rang and we all froze, just as if we were playing musical statues. Then we remembered we were in a public place, surrounded by lots of people who were having a normal day. We started to move again, in a kind of ever-so-casual way. Paul answered the phone in a calm and collected manner, but it was to do with something else, so we started to meander around the paintings again.

There's only so much meandering you can do, so eventually we gave it up and headed back to the hotel. I fussed around my hotel room, making tea, dipping biscuits, waiting for something to happen. When it got to half past four I had convinced myself that there was a good chance the jury wouldn't be back that day. I took off my boots and got myself settled into a chair to watch a Harry Potter film on Sky. We didn't have Sky at home and I figured I might as well make the most of it.

As the opening titles were rolling and I was deciding I had actually managed to find a film I'd not seen before, there was what sounded like an explosion on my door as Paul's wife banged and shouted, 'The jury's got a verdict.'

Could I get my boots on my feet? Not a chance. They got all tangled up and I hobbled off across the quadrant to the court trying to telephone and text several people while putting on my cardigan, all at the same time. I rushed over with Helen Cull, Paul Morten and Anna Morten, with Helen saying she hoped we wouldn't miss it and us reminding her it was highly unlikely they'd start without her. The front entrance of the court was packed and we had to run up eight flights of stairs because the lifts were so full. By the time I got in there, the lower part of the courtroom was packed and there was only standing room available.

As I looked around, I saw Joe Karam, his family and his partner, the lawyers' partners, police officers, a lot of journalists and a small gathering of well-known media personalities. The jury was brought in and there was nothing to be read from their faces. Nothing at all. I expected I'd be able to tell one way or the other but there was nothing to be seen. They didn't look at anyone in particular, although a couple of them checked the public gallery, maybe for friendly faces. As they settled in, David Bain was brought into the courtroom and put in the dock. Excuse the cliché but you could have cut the tension with a knife when the court clerk asked the jury forewoman if they had reached a unanimous decision. She looked around and checked with the others, which I hadn't expected her to do (they don't do that on the telly — serves me right for believing what I see on TV) and then she was asked how they found the defendant, David Cullen Bain, on the first charge, the murder of Robin Bain, to which she replied, 'Not guilty.'

The whole court knew that if that charge was a not guilty then the other four would be too. There were cheers from the public gallery and an almost deafening clack of journalists' laptop keyboards. I couldn't see the faces of the prosecution lawyers because they stayed facing forwards, which meant they had their backs to the rest of the court. David Bain was struggling to hold it together as the rest of the verdicts were read out. And by 4.43 p.m. on Friday, 5 June 2009 it was over. Or was it?

I left the courtroom at that point, just out of interest to see how busy it had been upstairs in the public gallery and in the viewing room but was swept away in the tide of people coming the other way. I heard lots of people saying it was the right verdict and I saw a few faces I recognised because they'd spent more time watching this retrial than me.

Then there was the media scrum afterwards and the attempt to get out of the building. The front doors were closed and locked so we had to go out of the side entrance — I got the distinct impression that this kind of media response in high-profile cases wasn't unusual at this court because the security guards were well organised and, as they had been throughout, very nice. It wouldn't have been appropriate for me to go through the doors with the defence team so I squeezed through the side door and into the waiting throng of humanity that had materialised in the advancing twilight. A pregnant woman was so overcome with emotion she threw up in the bushes. People were milling about, talking on phones and waiting for the defence team to come out of the building. I have to admit to walking off at that point because I couldn't hear anything from where I was and it was more interesting for me to watch the watchers than it was to hear what was being said at the microphone. Not because I didn't want to, but I'd just spent several months with the defence team — I could always ask them what was said and I knew it would be on the TV later on. And on and on …

Most people were on the phone. One man was shouting into a phone he had lodged between his ear and his shoulder and was texting into each of two other phones he was holding — I admired his manual dexterity. Someone asked me if I was the doctor. When I asked which one and found they had meant Laniet's GP they were disappointed, and I felt strangely anonymous, which was an odd thing to feel, considering that I was.

After the speeches had been made and the initial furore had died down, Joe Karam, David Bain and the defence team took their leave and walked back to the hotel. Unfortunately, one of the reporters had missed them leaving and asked me if they'd got in a car and driven off. I said yes because I thought that if she was really a good reporter she shouldn't have taken her eye off the biggest story of the year while it walked off down the road — surrounded, I might add, by a massive entourage of cameras and lights, the glow of which could be seen across the park. I wandered back to the hotel and sat down for five minutes in my room to gather my thoughts.

What were my thoughts? I didn't really have any. Here I was, at the heart of one of New Zealand's biggest ever court and news stories and I had absolutely no thoughts whatsoever. Strange. Or maybe it's normal. With hindsight, I think it was just pure exhaustion. All I did know was that I was tired but I went upstairs to Joe Karam's suite to see what was happening. What met my eyes was an open door and what seemed to be a free-for-all of people arriving, people I hadn't seen at the court or in the public gallery, so I tinkered with the idea of whether they'd just wandered in of their own accord (apparently some of them had) and whether anyone actually knew them all. My thoughts were soon interrupted by the arrival of John Campbell, Carol Hirschfeld and a cameraman or two. As John Campbell interviewed Joe Karam, I was leaning against a wall at the back of the room when my phone rang in my pocket. I sneaked out of the sliding doors onto the balcony to answer it, whereupon a friend of mine announced he could see me on TV but, oh my goodness, where had I gone now? I told him I'd come outside because some idiot had rung me when I was on the TV.

The rest of the evening is a blur of exhaustion. It reaches a point when you realise that the only thing you have in common with anyone in the room is this case. I had no idea what things most of the defence team did or liked outside work and I had no energy left to find out; I would have been quite happy to sit and watch the spectacle before me. I eventually went to bed far later than I should have done and I remember being woken up at about 5 a.m. by revellers singing rude songs.

The next thing I remember was checking out of the hotel to go home as TV crews from all the major stations plus radio passed through the foyer to go and interview Joe Karam and David Bain in the garden. The TV3 news presenter told me I looked tired and I was so exhausted I could barely form a reply so I got in the taxi and went to the airport. As I sat waiting for my flight to be called, I played a little game. I had a newspaper on my knee in which were several photographs, including my own. I wondered if anyone would recognise me. They didn't, so I was happy to fall asleep on the plane with my head lolling, safe in the knowledge that no one would point at me with any recognition of my having recently been involved with the Trial of the Century.

Epilogue

According to one of his books, when he's standing in the check-out queue at the supermarket, forensic psychologist Nigel Latta likes to look at what people buy and then practise some psychological profiling. I like to look around and see how many types of evidence I can spot and how I'd trace a person who came into the shop to make purchases. Are they buying food for someone they've got trapped in a basement? If I had to recall for a police officer, could I remember what the man in front of me was wearing? What vehicle was he driving? Is that child crying tears of frustration or tears of fear? I guess it's a function of our different roles in life but I note that neither Mr Latta's nor my household ever has all the things we need in the house and someone's always at the supermarket buying something essential.

Today it was butter. While I was buying butter and sizing up the footwear mark on the floor, I thought about regret, because I assumed that if the mark on the floor had been a crime scene mark, the person who caused it would have regretted it when it was matched, by a forensic scientist, to their right shoe and, if I had to do an independent review, I'd probably agree with the Crown's expert, because it was a very clear mark.

I've always said that I've never regretted anything I've done in my life. Sitting around waiting for life to happen to you is a waste of time. You have to get out there and make good things happen. I did that and here I am. I have no idea what the future holds but you can be sure that I won't be sitting around waiting for it to come to me.

References

Over the years, I have learnt an enormous amount through my training, experience and anecdotal information. However, forensic science, just like any other area of science, has an enormous body of research behind it. There are just too many relevant articles to list them all but those to which I have referred either directly or generally are listed below.

Adams, D. 1985. *So Long, and Thanks for All the Fish*, Pan Macmillan, London and Sydney.

Barni, F., Lewis, S., Berti, A., Miskelly, G. & Lago, G. 2007. Forensic application of the luminol reaction as a presumptive test for latent blood detection. *Talanta*, **72**, 896–913.

Baselt, R. 2001. *Drug Effects on Psychomotor Performance*, Biomedical Publications, Foster City, California.

Bass, B. & Jefferson, J. 2003. *Death's Acre: inside the legendary 'Body Farm'*, Time Warner, London.

Brown, A. 2006. The use of forensic botany and geology in war crimes investigations in NE Bosnia. *Forensic Science International*, **163**, 204–210.

Caddy, B. (ed) 2001. *Forensic Examination of Glass and Paint*, Taylor & Francis, London.

Copperfield, D. 2007. *Wasting Police Time: the crazy world of the war on crime*, Monday Books, Great Britain.

Coulson, S. A., Gummer, A. B. & Triggs, C. M. 2001. Glass on clothing and shoes of members of the general population and people suspected of breaking crimes. *Scientific and Technical*, **41**, 39–48.